I dedicate this book to my daughter Angelique.
Angelique you are amazing, I love you with all my
heart, you inspire me every day - BIG KISS TO YOU!
xxx

Detox

RECIPE BOOK

written by
celebrity trainer

Christianne Wolff

About the Author

Christianne Wolff is an award-winning weight loss expert, yoga and Pilates instructor, writer and healer.

She is internationally recognised as one of the leading experts in fitness and weight loss, and is passionate about using foods to heal.

Christianne writes several columns for the national press and has appeared in over one hundred national magazines over the last seventeen years. She has trained many celebrities and hundreds of clients over the last two decades.

Christianne owns The Body Rescue Fitness and Well-being centres with her husband Robbie, and they run Luxury Detox and Fitness holidays around the world.

Her book The Body Rescue Plan was a best seller on national TV.

For more information on Christianne, go to;

www.thebodyrescueplan.com

b·r

Published by

Filament Publishing Ltd
16, Croydon Road, Beddington, Croydon, Surrey CR0 4PA
+44 (0)20 8688 2598
www.filamentpublishing.com

ISBN 978-1-910819-31-9

Designed by

L.K. Banks
www.louisebanks.com

Printed in the Czech Republic through Akcent Media

DISCLAIMER: Before starting this programme you may wish to seek medical advice from a doctor and get permission to start The Body Rescue detox Plan. The advice and instruction in The Body Rescue Detox Plan does not replace any medical procedure. Christianne Wolff disclaims any liability or loss. The Body Rescue Detox plan is not recommended if you are pregnant, or breastfeeding.

Contents

A BIG
Thank you
TO:

Robbie my husband for being an amazing help whilst cooking endless recipes.

My mum for helping with some of the recipes too for the shoot

Angelique for eating all the food !

Lou Banks, my wonderful designer who is an absolute joy to work with.

And Andres Le Sauvage photographer for coming to Portugal with me and taking some awesome photos!

Paul Magee for the wonderful food photos in my book and his wife Sarah Magee for helping cook some of the recipes for the shoot.

And also a big thank you to everyone who has supported me, followed me, and shown me love, I send you loads of love back!

The Body Rescue Detox Recipe Book

Foreword

"Like most people I lead a pretty busy life, I often work 12 hour days, which means I got into a viscous cycle with food. I was busy, I got tired and I ate what I thought wasn't a bad diet, but I would drink more wine than I should, I got tired, I put on weight....and so it went on.

I've tried so my diets in my time and whilst I have lost weight in the past I haven't been able to keep it off and I also seemed to lose energy.

I decided to try Christianne's detox but Initially approached the plan with scepticism. I'm in my 50's and it just seemed too much like hard work. I also had what I called "events" in my diary, like family dinners, girls weekends away, work lunches etc so how could I ever fit a detox in and stick to it?

However the book is so easy to follow, and the meal plans and recipes really open your eyes to how delicious these foods are.

There are some amazing recipes which are so straightforward to follow. My regular favourites are the nut bread which I make at the weekend and then eat during the week and the others I love include the courgette noodles which I serve with her poached salmon dish.

The first few days are fun because it's all new then it becomes a bit tougher and I did get headaches and felt tired, but then from day 6 all of a sudden I felt amazing! My energy levels soared, my eyes were wider and brighter and I was happier and not as moody (as I was told!) and my stomach was much flatter. Plus I slept so much better. By the end of the 2 weeks I had lost 9lbs but more importantly I felt fantastic and everyone said I looked amazing.

Secondly I found the mindset work extremely powerful. It gave me focus and also helped me to understand why I was eating and drinking so much.

And as for the "events" in the diary if I was out I would ask for food that had no sugar or dairy added. If I was at a family do I would explain before I turned up what I was doing and people were so supportive and at work in lunch meetings I would take my fish salad and fruit and watch everyone have sandwiches and chocolate! And by about 3pm most people would be feeling drowsy whilst I was full of beans.

I have to say this was quite a life changing time for me and Christianne is incredible. She has developed something that is easy and straightforward to follow and achieves quite amazing results. Also it has changed how I cook and how I eat and it has also changed how I think about what I eat,which has meant I have not just kept the weight off, but I have lost even more (now 2 stone 7 pounds) So go for it! Two weeks out of a lifetime is a very, very short period of time but it could have life changing results!"

Helen Burgess – Property Director for Theo Paphitis

Testimonials & Media

The Body Rescue
Plan

as seen in

A BRAND NEW ATTITUDE
woman&home Bodyfit SOUL&SPIRIT SPIRIT&DESTINY

Men's Fitness COSMOPOLITAN women's fitness celebs on sunday

ultra FIT NOW Zest magazine SHAPE Womans Weekly

WORK LBC 97.3FM Reveal .co.uk msn health & fitness

DAILY EXPRESS The Mail ON SUNDAY GRAZIA

HEALTH&FITNESS SPORTS MAGAZINE London Evening Standard The Daily Telegraph

DAILY Mirror HELLO! OK! FIRST FOR CELEBRITY NEWS eve

your wellness the gateway to living well FT FINANCIAL TIMES THE HUFFINGTON POST Closer

Sweaty Betty

Healthy the guardian

love the recipes
in this book?

Then head over to

*Facebook &
Twitter*

and let us know
what you think!

 www.facebook.com/TheBodyRescuePlan

 christianne_w

Bella

"Put on a few pounds? No problem, lose them fast with Christianne's simple cleansing plan!"

marie claire
THINK SMART, LOOK AMAZING

*"Wondering how you can boost your weight loss? These are the **best** fat-burning breakfasts that will also keep you full until lunch..."*

LOOK
Britain's Best Selling Fashion Magazine

"Check out Christianne's recipes for some super tasty and healthy recipe ideas. Brilliant, easy to cook and satisfying!"

Your comments from

facebook

Caroline Macdonald Ok, so here goes. I have lost 13lbs in total. 3lbs in the 3 days before I started, by trying out the smoothies and juices for breakfast. Then 10lbs in the 2 weeks that I have been on the plan. My measurements and before and after shots are just while I have been on the plan. I have lost 1 inch each off my chest, hips and thighs and 1 1/2 inches off my waist. I feel so much healthier and have more energy. I do not feel that I have been on a diet, but rather a healthy eating plan. I have never felt hungry or deprived. My finger nails are growing and are strong. I am wearing clothes that I previously could not fit into. So I feel amazing at the moment. Still need to lose more, but a huge thanks to you Christianne for starting me on the right path.

Angie Henry Caroline Macdonald you look great, Well done!! I've lost 6ibs now in the 2 weeks. My stomach feels so much better for doing this and I have not craved the weekly take away that I would normally have with my teenagers. My bowel movement is a bit sluggish so may try some hydrotherapy. My sleepless nights have siezed which I so pleased about and the meditations have been a God send. Thank you Christianne Wolff for enlightening me to make some sensible changes X

Mandy Hill Hi I've lost 6lbs in the 2 weeks and yes I feel better. Stomach gone down and as Sian says I feel more in control of what I eat. I'm going to follow the book and reintroduce foods but keep to the portion control which I think is important. So sorry Dee Jones that must be frustrating for you. Maybe you didn't have much to lose? Sometimes that's harder. Hope Christianne Wolff can help you x

Katy Leonard Hi Christiane. I feel so much better after following your regime over the last 12days and would definitely like to sign up for the full 12 week plan. I am sorely tempted by all the chocolate and will miss my roast lamb on Easter Day but I shall try not to give in! However my husband's family have a huge celebration next week which will involve a lunch and then an evening meal at super eating places. I will be seen as very antisocial if I refuse to have a drink of champagne. Will this be too tragic? I shall choose the most healthy options available on the menus and will get straight back to the plan as soon as I can.

Joselyn Smith End of the 2 week detox, I have lost 7lbs in total, 1 inch off my waist, thighs and bust, 3 inches of my hips. My stomach is flatter because it isn't so bloated. I can honestly say I haven't felt hungry at all, I do miss a cup of tea with a splash of milk. I can see how this will become a way of life. I am delighted with the weight loss as the exercise part was always going to be an issue as I am waiting for a knee replacement, I do the best I can exercisewise. I have booked a facial as a treat/reward for myself. I am so glad I jumped off the fence and decided to do this plan, I am sleeping better and don't wake up with that "is it morning already" feeling. Christianne you are an inspiration, thank you.

Taj phull @tajjy2011 · Feb 1
@Christianne_W week 3 starts and im already 11 lbs down. Come on the rescue plan.
↩ ⟲ 1 ★ 2 •••

Patsy Collyer @patsycollyer · 5h
@Christianne_W @TheHuntley Will do. Thank you! This plan is a revelation! :)
↩ ⟲ 1 ★ 1 •••
View conversation

Patsy Collyer @patsycollyer · 7h
@Christianne_W @TheHuntley Day 9 of the BRP detox and I'm forcing myself to eat. No hunger pangs whatsoever! :) x
↩ ⟲ 1 ★ 1 •••

Patsy Collyer @patsycollyer · 30m
@Christianne_W @TheHuntley Two weeks doing the detox and my 'tight' jeans are loose... Can't wait for week 12! thebodyrescueplan.com
↩ ⟲ ★ 1 •••

Penni Rowe @sparkle0918 · 3h
@Christianne_W better than ever my partner and I have lost over 2 st put together & we're only in wk 6 we feel much healthier & energized x
↩ ⟲ 1 ★ 1 •••
View conversation

Gracie McLaven @graciemclaven · Feb 23
@Christianne_W - @AliMclaven and I have had a fab 1st week on the plan, both 8lbs lighter as well!
↩ ⟲ 1 ★ 1 •••

Download Your Free Meditation CD Now!

To download your FREE meditation CD please go to the following link http://www.thebodyrescueplan.com/meditation-audio-request/ and enter the code:

TBRP1

Please note you cannot download directly onto a phone or iPad. To get the meditations onto your phone or iPad you can download to your computer onto iTunes and then this can upload to your phone or iPad.

Visit the website!

Do you want support when you do the detox? Would you like more;

- recipe ideas
- shopping lists
- videos of mindset
- videos of exercises

and more...

then check out my website
www.thebodyrescueplan.com
and sign up to the Body Recue Plan Membership!

2 WEEK Detox Plan

Download of
The Body Rescue Plan Book

Support emails everyday

Videos of Mindset

Videos of Abs exercises

Videos of Recipes

Daily recipes and Shopping plan
for 2 weeks

Daily Meditations

Weight loss up to 10 pounds!

12 WEEK The Body Rescue Plan

6 MONTH Life Long Plan

The Body Rescue Plan	Life Long Plan
Download of The Body Rescue Plan Book	Download of The Body Rescue Plan Book
Support emails everyday	Support emails once a week
The Body Rescue Plan in Video form	Daily teachings every day
Videos of Mindset	Videos of Maintenance Mindset
Videos of Abs exercises	Videos of Abs exercises (updated every 2 months)
Videos of Interval exercises	Videos of Interval exercises (updated every 2 months)
Videos of Resistance exercises	Videos of Resistance exercises (updated every 2 months)
Videos of Yoga exercises	Videos of Yoga exercises
Videos of Recipes	Videos of Recipes
Daily recipes and Shopping plan for 12 weeks	Daily recipes and Shopping plan for 12 weeks
Daily Meditations	Daily Maintenance Meditations
Weight loss up to 2 stone 10 pounds!	Monthly LIVE group call with me!
	Sustain your weight loss with a Life Long Plan and have Weight control forever!

Introduction

Welcome to The Body Rescue Detox Recipe Book!

This is part of my programme, The Body Rescue Plan, which is a twelve-week plan that enables you to lose weight through mindset, detoxing, fitness and yoga. However, you can also choose to do the detox element separately from the twelve-week plan – it's great for when you feel you need your energy boosting, want to lose a few pounds, want to lose that bloated / tired feeling, and when you want to cleanse your system. I would advise you do the detox programme no more than four times a year, so every three months or so is ideal.

I have written this recipe book due to sheer volume of demand – people were calling out for it. I received emails every day from people who loved my plan, but needed more ideas for breakfast, lunch and dinner during the detox phase. Everyone seems to struggle with ideas for what to eat when their foods are more limited. But actually, what is really exciting is that your food isn't limited at all. In fact, you will discover new foods you have never come across before, or never cooked with before, you will become far more creative and you will get a new taste for healthy, delicious foods that make you feel healthy, happy and more vibrant in life.

After that you can choose to use those recipes in everyday life and your mind will be opened up to a more wonderful, exciting future!

To make life easier for you, I have written meal plans based on the following categories:

Summer

Winter

Vegetarian

Fast food / quick recipes

I have also laid out the recipes under the following headings:

 Smoothies & juices

 Breakfasts

 Snacks

 Lunch & Supper dishes

Why Detox?

CHAPTER 1

Why Detox?

If our bodies weren't overloaded by the pollution in the air we breathe, water we drink and food we eat, a detox wouldn't be necessary.

However, our diet now contains so much animal protein, saturated and trans-fats, caffeine, sugar and alcohol that the body's natural detoxification processes aren't able to cope. Imagine if you produced two buckets of trash each day but only one got taken away . the extra trash would build up and build up and become overwhelming, until you took positive action to do something about it.

That's what our bodies are trying to cope with. Our organs – the colon, liver, kidneys, lungs, lymph and skin – which were once capable of eliminating and neutralising toxins, are now completely overloaded to the point where toxic material remains inside our tissues. Our bodies try to protect us from them by surrounding them with mucus and fat so that they will not cause an imbalance or trigger an immune response, but the fact is if we don't take positive action, they won't be cleared from the body.

That's where a detox comes in. A special detoxing and cleansing diet gives your body a massive boost and helps it to get back on track. Even if your diet is normally good, an internal clean can revitalise your system and rid your body of harmful bacteria, viruses and parasites.

Many of us are struggling to shed the extra pounds we're carrying – no matter what we do, they just won't budge and we become unhappy and stressed, and often try to cheer ourselves up with more of the things that are causing the problems in the first place. If that's your experience, then know this – it's not all your fault. If your body is sluggish and overburdened with toxicity, it can affect not only your motivation to lose weight, but also your body's ability to shed the pounds. Undertaking a detox can help with this and by following the rules, you can start to make the progress you've craved.

It's not just about food, either – exercise, meditation and yoga all play a part, and regular skin brushing, hot baths, saunas, and sweating, as well as regularly getting out in the country and breathing in fresh air, will also help your body rid itself of toxins.

How to Detox

CHAPTER 2

How to Detox

With my Body Rescue Detox System, I advise you to cut out:

- Gluten
- Dairy
- Alcohol
- Sugar
- Caffeine
- Processed Foods

Detoxing is intended to clear out the toxins from your body so that everything functions as it should. Your liver and colon do most of the work and if they are cleansed, then they will work more efficiently. Your liver controls how many calories you burn a day, so if it's in top working order then your metabolism will be on fire.

We eat to meet the nutritional needs of our body, and consuming foods full of toxins does not provide our cells with the nutrients they need to grow and repair. Consequently the body sends a signal to consume more until those needs are met and so we overeat, but still consume poor quality foods, and without the correct nutrients the body becomes diseased.

Wheat & gluten

Wheat has little nutritional value and digestion of both wheat and gluten is exceptionally difficult. Chances are you will be intolerant to wheat and gluten and not even realise – bloating, headaches, and tiredness are common side effects of gluten intolerance.

More and more people are discovering that eliminating wheat from their diet brings positive results. Everything from psoriasis to migraine headaches, and heart disease to arthritis, can be improved.

So why is wheat intolerance such an epidemic in the twenty-first century? The wheat we eat today has been so heavily processed it barely resembles the wheat of our ancestors. Dr William Davis of The Heart Scan Blog places a lot of the blame on the dwarf mutant variant, which is estimated to make up ninety-nine per cent of the wheat used today.

Other researchers disagree. In his book Detoxification and Healing, Dr Sidney MacDonald Baker has researched an enzyme in the gut that's responsible for breaking down gluten – the DPP4 enzyme. According to Dr Baker, gluten-intolerant people have this enzyme missing, or else it's underactive. If gluten goes undigested, it causes problems both in the gut and in the bloodstream. This change may be caused by toxicity in our environment and the food chain.

Another suggestion is that consuming grain was never part of our make-up. As humans we only started farming ten thousand years ago, yet we have had hundreds of millions of years as hunter-gatherers.

Whatever the cause, avoiding wheat or gluten seems to be a positive change everyone can make to their diet. I've personally witnessed my clients' health improve dramatically just through making this small change.

Dairy

If you are wondering where to get your calcium from without eating milk and cheese, you can actually get all you need from green vegetables, the darker the better. Nuts are also a fantastic source of calcium, almonds in particular. Cows' milk is good for you if you are a calf, but we do not have the same digestive system as a cow and therefore it is not beneficial to us. During pasteurisation many enzymes are destroyed, as well as vitamins and good bacteria.

Those countries with the lowest rate of dairy consumption (Africa and Asia) have the lowest rate of osteoporosis, and the countries that have the biggest consumption of dairy (America and the UK) have the highest rate of osteoporosis. Foods that contain vitamin D are also beneficial to bone health.

Yogurt is allowed in week 2 as it contains natural good bacteria for your gut and as its fermented (partially digested) so does not react in the same way to your body as milk!

Alcohol

Alcohol is a liquid sugar and does not hold any nutritional value for the body. The body experiences a huge release of insulin when you drink alcohol, which then informs your brain there is a mass of energy available, so the body stops burning fat and retains it instead.

Sugar

Sugar is highly addictive and has no nutritional value for the body. All it will do for you is contribute to an enormous amount of today's illnesses, including diabetes and weight gain.

What does sugar do to your body?

As long as you ingest anything containing fructose or sucrose (table sugar) you will be unable to cure yourself of high blood pressure, heart disease or diabetes.

A word of warning ... if you want to continue to drink fizzy drinks, but think you will get by with drinking artificially sweetened fizzy drinks, you should know that aspartame is a neurological toxin. So you have the choice of using a liver toxin (sugar) or a neurotoxin (NutraSweet) or you could just give up fizzy drinks altogether. Or why not have fizzy water with a squeeze of lemon instead?

Eating whole fruits does not cause the same problem as high fructose corn syrup and table sugar, because the fruits contain vitamins, minerals, and antioxidants which help metabolise the fructose.

While high fructose corn syrup is the number one food substance which creates the metabolic syndrome of diabetes, high blood pressure, liver disease, kidney disease, and vascular disease, the number two food substance is the yeast used to make beer.

Some of the other effects of sugar on the body are:

- Increases overgrowth of candida yeast organism.
- Increases chronic fatigue.
- Can make it difficult to lose weight because of constantly high insulin levels, which causes the body to store excess carbs as fat.
- Can increase or intensify symptoms of anxiety and panic in susceptible women.
- Increases anxiety and irritability.
- Increases tooth decay.
- Increases hyperactivity in about fifty per cent of children.
- Can trigger binge-eating in those with bulimia.
- Increases PMS symptoms.
- Drinking fructose raises uric acid levels, which also increases the risk of diabetes and high blood pressure.

Why do we get sugar cravings?

Research has shown that sugar acts on the brain the same way that class A drugs do. Sugar raises serotonin levels which makes us feels good, and when that starts to wear off we want more.

We also use it as a pick-me-up. Sugar and caffeine are a dangerous combination as they over stimulate the body. This can become a vicious cycle as our body starts to depend on this quick fix for energy.

How to curb sugar cravings

You can reduce sugar cravings by:

- Reducing or eliminating caffeine.
- Reducing or eliminating diet drinks and processed fruit juices.
- Keeping the carbs low and eating plenty of protein and vegetables.
- Reducing or eliminating high GL foods.
- Ensuring you have enough B vitamins, which are for energy production.
- Having enough chromium and magnesium, which can help reduce sugar cravings.
- Getting plenty of sleep which, as well as giving your body the rest it needs, helps balance hormones.

- Looking after your adrenal glands (get enough sleep, reduce stress, get enough vitamins C and B5, drink liquorice tea).
- Taking a good quality fish oil – great for elevating mood, amongst other things.
- Keeping a food diary and noting when you are getting the cravings.
- Eating a small amount of dark chocolate (minimum seventy per cent cocoa solids) if cravings are really bad.
- Drinking raw cacao (mix with hot water and coconut milk) as it's great for cravings.
- Eating half a banana before bed, and getting plenty of sunshine and fresh air to help raise serotonin levels.

Caffeine

Caffeine will make the body's energy levels fluctuate, which in turn signals the need for sugary foods, so steer clear.

Processed foods

Processed foods have been processed to within an inch of their life. They have no nutritional value whatsoever and they are packed full of toxins which are damaging to the body. The toxins wreak havoc within the body and end up being stored within the fat cells to keep them away from the important organs.

Things That Hurt Your Body

CHAPTER 3

Things That Hurt Your Body

Monosodium glutamate

You will all be familiar with the saying, one pop and you can't stop. Well, there is a reason for that – monosodium glutamate (MSG). It's the cocaine of the food world.

MSG is a flavour enhancer; it overstimulates the glutamate receptors of the brain, intensifying the flavour of the food, which then makes it hard to stop eating it – you become addicted to that food.

Glutamic acid is an amino acid that occurs naturally in some foodstuffs – and some food manufacturers employ scientists who will tell you there is no difference between naturally occurring free glutamate in food and the manufactured type found in MSG. However, this is not the case. The process of artificially manufacturing glutamate means it is broken down and the naturally occurring glutamate is changed into free forms never found in nature, so they react completely differently inside the body.

Modified glutamate is absorbed extremely quickly into the gastrointestinal tract, where it spikes blood plasma levels of glutamate. Glutamic acid is known as an excitotoxin. High levels of excitotoxins have been shown in studies on rats to cause damage to areas of the brain and humans are five to six times more sensitive!

What are excitotoxins?

Excitotoxins are substances that overexcite brain and nerve cells, and they over excite the cell until it dies. This is where certain symptoms kick in :
- migraines
- lethargy
- ADHD and ADD
- cardiac arrhythmia
- dizziness
- depression
- rapid heartbeat

to name but a few!

Aspartame

BEWARE!

Aspartame causes:

- headaches
- migraines
- dizziness
- seizures
- nausea
- depression
- weight gain
- tachycardia
- rashes
- anxiety attacks
- fatigue

Are you really going to ingest something that causes over ninety different symptoms, including the list opposite? Yet we do and – even worse – we give it to our children.

Aspartame accounts for over seventy-five per cent of adverse reactions to food additives reported to the US Food and Drug Administration (FDA). Aspartame is also an excitotoxin. It overexcites your brain cells to the point of death, and excitotoxins have also been shown to stimulate the production of free radicals (which can cause cancer).

Aspartame is made up of the following: aspartic acid, phenylalanine and methanol.

Aspartic acid and phenylalanine are amino acids found naturally in the body; however, the aspartic acid within aspartame is not what is found naturally within the body, it is changed into a free form never found in nature. So once you have ingested aspartame your cells are being excited to death.

Phenylalanine can cross the blood-brain barrier and, just like aspartic acid, when levels are artificially increased, it can create an unhealthy balance.

Phenylalanine is a contributor to mental health problems. Due to its ability to cross the blood-brain barrier it can cause serotonin to be decreased, which in turn can lead to depression. If you or anyone you are close to have ever been prescribed anti-depressants you will know their job is to increase serotonin within the brain.

Methanol

Methanol is a wood alcohol poison. When you drink aspartame, it breaks down above 85°C into amino acids and methanol. Methanol then breaks down into formaldehyde (a known carcinogen), formic acid and diketopiperazine (DKP) which is a brain tumour agent.

Is this really something you or your children want to be ingesting?

Recreational drugs

The three most commonly used recreational drugs in the Western world are caffeine, tobacco and alcohol. These can all have harmful effects, putting a load on your liver, and they take valuable nutrients out of your body, making you more susceptible to acidity, which leads to disease. Aim to eliminate them, or at least cut back.

Things That Help Your Body

CHAPTER 4

Things That Help Your Body

Coconut oil

Unlike other oils derived from vegetables, coconut oil does not become unstable or carcinogenic when cooked at a high temperature.

Coconut oil was once believed to be a 'bad fat' by doctors as ninety per cent of the fat it contains is saturated fat; this immediately sounded warning bells for a lot of people. However, of the ninety per cent of saturated fat within coconut oil – which consists mostly of highly beneficial medium-chain triglycerides – fifty per cent comes from lauric acid. There is only one other place you will find lauric acid naturally and that is in breast milk.

The body converts lauric acid into monolaurin, which has absolutely outstanding anti-viral, anti-fungal, anti-microbial properties. This makes lauric acid a fantastic defence for the human body against diseases like athlete's foot, measles, herpes, flu, swine flu, hepatitis C . the list goes on. There is also research into how it can help people with HIV / AIDS. Are you seeing how fantastic coconut oil is? Basically it strengthens your entire immune system.

The other fantastic thing about coconut oil is that it is natural – there are no toxic side effects which you would get from trying to treat all of the above with pharmaceutical drugs – but to do all of these wonderful things the body must be able to produce monolaurin. The only way to do this is to have an abundance of lauric acid, as without lauric acid the body cannot make monolaurin.

You might be asking yourself, what about the saturated fat? Isn't that bad?

It's important to know that not all saturated fats are alike. The medium-chain triglycerides found in coconut oil are not harmful. They will not raise your cholesterol levels or lead to an increase in low-density lipoprotein (LDL). In fact, coconut oil has been found to reduce injuries to the arteries and prevent atherosclerosis.

Coconut oil also has the added benefit of helping your metabolic rate; the medium-chain fatty acids in coconut oil are burned instantly on consuming it, which then boosts your thyroid levels for hours after – so coconut oil is a great addition if you have thyroid issues.

So, in short, coconut oil helps you lose weight, strengthens the immune system, is good for heart health, helps prevent free radical damage and does not spoil when heated to a high temperature, along with many more health benefits, so it is something worth putting in your diet.

Green vegetables.

Green vegetables are a nutrient dense source of minerals like magnesium, potassium, manganese, calcium, folate and betaine.

The Great Green Vegetables!

These are just a few super heroes of the veg world:

- Kale
- Chard
- Lettuce
- Parsley
- Spinach
- Sweet potato leaves
- Baby greens
- Endive

Magnesium

Your mitochondria use magnesium to produce the body's energy currency. Eating greens like spinach and chard will give you a good dietary supplement of magnesium.

Potassium

Potassium is responsible for nerve cell function, protein synthesis, muscle growth, and muscle contractions. If you get cramps you are probably lacking in potassium (or sodium).

Manganese

Manganese aids in the formation of bones.

Calcium

Leafy greens are a fantastic source of calcium, look what cows eat all day!

Folate

Helps prevent heart disease.

Betaine

Betaine also helps maintain liver health, and spinach is one of the best vegetable sources of betaine.

Make sure your eating plan is rich in green vegetables!

Chia seed

Chia seed is a superfood and is a complete protein, with eight essential amino acids. It is high in antioxidants, and contains seven times more vitamin C than oranges, three times more iron than spinach, and two times more potassium than bananas. It is great for healing the digestion, is high in fibre, and balances the blood sugar levels.

Buy from your local health food shop and have on smoothies, oats or yogurt.

Cruciferous vegetables

- Cauliflower (white or purple)
- Broccoli (green or purple)
- Brussels sprouts Kale (green or purple)
- Bok choy (Chinese cabbage or pak choi)
- Cabbage (green, red or purple)
- Collard greens
- Watercress
- Radish
- Broccoli sprouts
- Rocket
- Mustard greens
- Turnip

Supplements and foods that can help you in a detoxification

Spirulina – great for balancing the blood sugars.

Wheatgrass – contains 100 enzymes, 12 vitamins and 21 amino acids – great in smoothies / juices.

Linseeds / milled flaxseeds

Acidopholis – good bacteria for the gut.

Psyllium husks – very fibrous and fills you up.

Water

You may not know this, but if you do not drink enough water you will gain weight! Being dehydrated makes you FAT!

Why?

Because you are likely to eat more if you are dehydrated. The amount of calories you burn a day is controlled by your liver (metabolism) and if your kidneys are dehydrated, your liver won't function efficiently. You can get water retention if you don't drink enough, which can make you look swollen. Drinking water before a meal fills you up.

So make sure you drink two litres a day!

Juicing and blending

To help aid a detox it is a really good idea to juice some of your fruits and vegetables. You can use a blender for making fruit smoothies, or a vegetable juicer for vegetables and hard fruits like apples. Or, if you want an all singing, all dancing vegetable and fruit juicer that doesn't chuck out the pulp and can also make soups, get high speed blender.

The nutrients are easily absorbed. They have high levels of antioxiants and phytochemicals, which are protective against cellular damage. Green juices are high in chlorophyll, which is good for your red blood cells, and green vegetables aid weight loss. Red, purple and blue juices reduce inflammation in the body. Adding the cruciferous vegetable group to smoothies can aid weight loss.

Juicing and blending have different benefits, as juicing spits out the fibre and with blending you retain the whole fruit and / vegetable, so what are the benefits of each?

Benefits of juicing

When you juice you are removing the pulp – the fibre. And whilst fibre is very good for you, it also slows down the absorption of nutrients and some nutrients stay in the fibre. When you juice, you absorb one hundred per cent of the nutrients in your glass, whereas with blending some of the nutrients are still held in the fibre.

Benefits of blending

- When you blend you get the whole food, i.e. nothing gets spat out.
- You absorb the fibre in the food. This means that the smoothie is far richer and more filling than a juice.
- Because blending is so high in fibre, it can help you with your digestion.
- There is no waste with blending.
- Your insulin levels won't spike as much with blending as with juicing.
- There is usually less washing up!

Other Things To Consider

CHAPTER 5

Other Things To Consider

Bath products

Have a look at the products you use on your body and in your home. If you are about to do a pure detox, you don't want to put a heap of junk on your skin for your pores to soak up into your body again!

You can now get chemical-free make up everywhere, so buy it! Seriously, it's so much better for you.

Also look at creams, bath products, what you wash your clothes in, what you clean your dishes in, what you brush your teeth with... everything! You can even get chemical free paint.

The main product you don't want on your skin is sodium lauryl sulphate (SLS). It's potentially harmful to skin and hair. It cleans by corrosion and dries skin by stripping the protective lipids from the surface, so it can't effectively regulate moisture. And guess what – it's in everything! I bet if you look on your bath products (if they are not chemical free) it will be one of the first ingredients!
Another extremely serious problem is the connection of SLS with nitrate contamination. SLS reacts with many types of ingredients used in skin products and forms nitrosamines (nitrates). Nitrates are potential cancer causing carcinogenics.

You can clean effectively with bicarbonate of soda and / or vinegar. You can also use special cloths that require no cleaning product, like ENJO.

Have a look in your bathroom cupboard and remove deodorants with aluminium and chemicals.

There are a lot of healthy choices now at health food shops, online and through your health practitioner. You can use essential oils, like rose and jasmine for perfumes, organic and natural make-ups, natural deodorants, or bentonite clay with a couple of drops of essential oil. Coconut oil makes a great cleanser and moisturiser.

Put some Epsom salts or cactus plants around your computer to help ward against EMR (electromagnetic radiation). Switch off your Wi-Fi.

Purchase products like Geo-Cleanse to help get rid of harmful rays in the home from smart meters, Wi-Fi, mobile phones and geopathic stress.

Air your house daily, leaving the windows open as much as possible. Have the window open slightly at night, so you are breathing fresh air. Fans are wonderful ionizers for the air; invest in ceiling fans or overhead fans. Take electrical equipment out of your bedroom and use organic cotton or Bamboo sheets.

If you live in the city, see if you can get to the countryside at weekends, for less car fumes and environmental pollutants. There's nothing like nature and fresh air to renew the mind and body.

Mindset

Around The

Detox

CHAPTER 5

"Focus on what you are gaining on a detox, rather than what you are missing out on. If you focus on what you are missing out on, you will desire that. If you focus on what you are benefitting from, you will gain even more!"

Christianne Wolff

Mindset Around The Detox

I have written a lot about limiting beliefs, trigger points and gratitude in my book The Body Rescue Plan, and with it comes meditation recordings (see page 13) to help you unravel why you have self-sabotaged in the past and why you can't live without certain foods. If you have not got that book I would really recommend you get it and use the mindset chapters as these are really beneficial to get you through the 2-week detox.

Many people have a fear of giving up coffee or sugar or alcohol, they feel it's something they cannot get through the day without. And you know what? Thousands of people have followed my detox plan and thousands have contacted me saying how it's changed their life. Yes, the first four days might be tricky, but that's it; after that it's not difficult and you will feel far more amazing than you have felt before, and you will see the weight come off, too. Your energy levels will soar, you will be in a better mood (after the first four days), your skin condition will improve, your eyes will look brighter, your breath will smell more pleasant, you will look younger and be happier – not to mention all your internal organs will be younger and brighter, too. Why wouldn't you want to do it?

So focus on your limiting beliefs (i.e. your fears of not having tea and coffee etc.) and also your trigger points (the things that make you feel like you have to have these substances). Often it's a need for energy, but after four days your body suddenly gains its natural energy; the addiction has gone and you feel incredible. And then with the mindset work, you focus not on what you will miss, but what you will gain, and when you do that it's very powerful.

You will have a greater gratitude for life and for your amazing body, and will be treating your body with absolute love and care, which it needs and deserves.

Instead of thinking its 'boring' to be healthy, you'll be thinking it's amazing to be healthy, because you have new energy, a younger body, more fun, and more confidence.

Instead of thinking how you can't have all those sweet foods and your beloved coffee and tea, you'll be thinking how amazing it is that you have access to all those energy charging foods that taste so delicious – oh, and when you do a detox your taste buds come alive, so everything tastes fantastic!

Instead of thinking how scared you are, get really, really excited – my clients totally change their lives. It's really exciting and liberating to no longer be addicted to things that age you and make you gain weight.

And you can expect to lose up to 5-10 pounds in the two weeks!

Plan Ahead

CHAPTER 7

Plan Ahead

I love a good detox, it makes you clear the fog and feel incredible, but you are in quite a raw and sensitive state when you first begin, and it's important to be really prepared.

One of the reasons I have written this recipe book is to give you more ideas, to help you more with the preparation and to give you motivation and excitement for the plan. I want to make it as easy as possible for you so that when you start the plan it just glides easily and you enjoy the ride.

So, first of all look at your diary...

- When do you want to start this?
- What events / meetings have you got going on that will collide with your detox?
- How can you prepare to work around that?
- You may choose to start your detox after a big event or, if you have a hectic social or work life, there may be no time like the present!
- If you are starting the detox plan whilst you are busy there are many ways you can help the situation run smoothly.

One of my yoga students, Helen Burgess, started my detox plan and was panicking because she had to go to a dinner dance where the food was pre-ordered. I advised her to call the caterers up and specify what she wanted, and to give them plenty of notice. It actually took a lot to convince her that this is normal in the catering world, and people have specific needs all the time. Even so, she felt really uncomfortable initially about doing it, and said that perhaps she should just eat what was given to her and 'try her best'. I said, 'Why would you do that to yourself? You are letting someone else dictate what you eat, you do have the choice.' So although reticent she called the caterers up and asked if she could possibly have melon to start with, and fish (that was not fried) as a main, and a fruit salad for dessert.

Was this a problem? Of course not, they were delighted to help her and told her they deal with such requests all the time.

It really is not an issue, but somehow we make it one. This was actually a huge turning point for Helen, as she realised how in control she is. She went on to lose two stone on The Body Rescue Plan, and now takes my nut bread everywhere with her! Whenever there is a family party or a meeting she will take it with her, one, because she loves it and wants to offer it to others and two, because it stops her being in a position where she is forced to eat what is offered to her.

The main areas I hear that people stumble on a detox are:

- Board meetings
- Meetings in bars and restaurants
- Meeting up with friends for coffee
- Parties / dinner dances
- Going for a drink

So if you have any of those events to look forward to, be mindful of preparing around them in advance!

Board meetings

Take your own detox energy bars (see recipe page 144), nuts and seeds, seaweed, water, vegetable and fruit juice or Nakd bars. Make your own nut bread – this is from week two of the detox – and take it with you (see page 206). You may turn some heads initially, but guess what? No one in that meeting wants those horrible sandwiches that make them lose focus, and the biscuits that make them fall asleep, and the cakes that make them feel bloated; everyone wants nutritious, delicious foods that will get them through the day feeling fantastic, so show them the way. The more amazing you look and feel, the more people will follow suit.

Meetings in bars & restaurants

For some reason many people feel they have to impress in a business meeting by eating or drinking what the other person is having. If the other person they are in a meeting with has wine, or if they have a dessert, or if they have meat, they feel they have to have it as well. It's a strange mentality to me, but very normal to many of the clients I have worked with over the years. Even when in bars or having a meeting in a cafe, one of my clients suggested it would seem 'weird' to his clients for him to order water. How far removed we have become from what our bodies need. We only need water as a drink, our bodies are made up of over sixty per cent water, so how funny that it is now deemed to be a weird drink to order. Anyway, I made him see sense and now he does, in fact, order water!

Parties & dinner dances

As I said about my client Helen, if you have a party to go to where there is food, whether it's a friend's do, works' do or charity event, you can call up and request a meal in line with your dietary requirements; if you can do it on an aeroplane, then you can do it anywhere! I haven't eaten meat since I was twelve years old, so I am used to asking for a different meal in advance, and it's fine. You are not being a pain, you are just doing what's right for your body. Why should you cause your body more pain to make someone else feel less pain? That is their job, so it's part of the package for them; you should do what's right for you.

I haven't ever drunk tea or coffee in my life – not because I am puritanical, I just don't like it – so I am used to

Meeting up with friends for coffee

not having to do the whole 'cuppa' thing with everyone just to be sociable. I have had clients say that friends have invited them round for a cuppa, and they felt obliged to share the pot of tea, again to make their friend feel happier. In the long run if you are making your body and mind un-happier, it will reflect the happiness of others around you. So do what is right for you and be strong.

Going for a drink

This can be the trickiest one, but the best way to get around not drinking alcohol is to drive. No one expects it of you then, you don't have the pressure from others to drink, and you know yourself you can't be tempted, either. But don't let a detox interrupt your social life; glam yourself up, enjoy the night, choose fruit juices, water or non-alcoholic cocktails that don't have sugar in, and you still feel part of the night. Many of my clients will have a large wine glass filled with fizzy water and a slice of lemon, so it makes them feel like they are still part of the night.

What other situations might you be in where you have to prepare?

To be really successful at the detox and any plan where you have an end goal, you want to be prepared, you want to be very focused on what you want the end result to be, and you want to be the influencer – to influence others, rather than them making you feel like you have to change back to your old habits again.

What would you like to feel and look like after the 2-week detox?

Determination and a clear focus on goals are key to success. Life does not always go according to plan or as we want it to. You could have a meeting called at the last minute; you might not get home for your lunch like you wanted to; etc. So what contingency plan will you have if plan A didn't work? For instance, be prepared for the unexpected, so have fruit at work, have pre-made salads in the fridge if you are in a hurry, take snacks in your handbag, batch cook, etc.

What water should you drink?

The quality of tap water varies from region to region, depending on the quality and type of the source.

Bottled water

According to the International Bottled Water Association (IBWA), there are several types of bottled water:

- Spring water
- Mineral water
- Well water
- Artesian water
- Sparkling water
- Purified water

Most natural bottled water is minimally processed.

Whilst bottled water is in general better than tap water there are also some dangers with it, too.

Plastic bottles have been known to release harmful chemicals into the water, so if you have bottled water choose the glass variety.

Filtered water

You can get devices to treat the tap water to eliminate impurities, such as chlorine or lead.

They can be anything from a jug that sits in the fridge door to a filtration system you plumb in to your kitchen tap.

Oftentimes these systems improve the taste as well!

Herbal tea

As well as one of my clients saying it's weird to order water, I had another one dismiss herbal teas when I first suggested she had them as she didn't want to drink 'hippy teas'. She has nothing against hippies, but it was her association that it wasn't part of her lifestyle, and was somehow removed from her as it was for the open-toed sandal brigade. Of course, when I started to educate her as to the benefits of drinking herbal teas and the detrimental effect caffeine has on your body, she soon started to listen.

So if you are meeting up with friends in a coffee house, go for herbal teas or water, or perhaps they might offer a juice. If they don't, why not suggest going somewhere that offers healthier snacks and vegetable juices? The more you can influence others to be healthier, the easier it will be for you.

The benefits of herbal tea

Herbal teas have many medicinal properties and come in delicious flavours and varieties. They can help with cravings, restore your energy, help with indigestion and more.

My favourite herbal teas at the moment are the Pukka brand. Whatever you choose, make sure they come from a good source.

Herbal teas need to be brewed for 5–10 minutes to get the full, healing properties.

Peppermint tea
Relieves symptoms of abdominal gas and bloating and is good for nausea. Peppermint tea can also be made using fresh herbs from the garden – and it's one of the easiest herbs to grow.

Ginger tea
Drinking ginger tea both stimulates and soothes the digestive system, and helps with nausea. It is anti-inflammatory, so can help sore joints too. You can make your own ginger tea by cutting a small slice of ginger and allowing it to brew.

Rooibos tea

This tea is high in vitamin C and other minerals and is grown in South Africa. It has many antioxidant properties and is anti-ageing.

Milk thistle and dandelion tea

Milk thistle or dandelion teas are gentle liver cleansers; they can also help our digestion.

Rosehip tea

From the fruit of the rose plant, this herbal tea is one of the best plant sources of vitamin C, which helps the adrenals and immune system.

Chamomile tea

Chamomile comes from a flower and helps the body relax. Many prefer to have this tea before they go to bed to help induce sleep and combat insomnia. It also can help soothe indigestion.

Nettle

Nettle tea is made with the leaves of stinging nettle. It can help anaemia, high blood pressure, rheumatism, arthritis, coughs and colds, and helps cleanse the bladder.

Lavender tea

This has many healing properties. It can help lift your spirits, and also soothes the digestion and induces sleep.

Echinacea

This is a powerful herb that contains active substances that enhance the activity of the immune system, relieve pain, reduce inflammation and have antioxidant effects.

Rosemary tea

Rosemary can help your muscles to relax and it aids digestion. Rosemary tea also relieves coughs and mild asthma symptoms.

Cardamom tea

Cardamom is an evergreen plant that's grown mainly in India and Guatemala. Cardamom tea helps treat indigestion, prevents stomach pain, and relieves flatulence. It can also help with coughs.

Hot water and lemon

I also like to have hot water and lemon. This alkalises the body and feels fantastic on your digestion, especially at the start of the day.

The Rules

of the 2-Week

Detox

CHAPTER 8

The Rules of the 2-Week Detox

The rules of my detox programme are really simple to follow, and you needn't worry about feeling hungry – you'll have enough to eat to keep you feeling full. Remember, it's not about deprivation, it's about health!

What's more, after just three days you will feel fantastic. In fact, some people feel amazing from day one.

One thing to watch for is that you may get a headache from cutting out caffeine. I know we are a nation of tea and coffee drinkers, but it is my professional opinion that we are a nation of addicts with no real energy, and this is mainly due to our caffeine obsession. It's highly likely after three days the headaches will go, so make the change – you won't look back.

You may also have a few days when you crave sugar / carbs. This usually only lasts for two or three days, five days max, and two or three days of mild discomfort is worth a lifetime of feeling amazing. Just being in control of your foods and energy levels is really empowering.

During your detox you may also feel irritable, your skin may react when the toxins come out, or you may get flu-like symptoms. It really depends how many toxins are in there, but the stronger the reaction, the more you must be resilient to the fight against those toxins. Get them out of you and start living!

Dried Fruit

I have allowed dried fruit in the detox plan. However, this will spike your insulin to a certain degree (although not in the same way as sugar) so see how your body feels when you eat it. Some people are more sensitive than others. Space it throughout the day.

PLEASE NOTE:

Please note the detox programme is not suitable for pregnant or breastfeeding women. If you have any doubts about your health, please contact your doctor prior to starting The Body Rescue 2-Week Detox Plan.

Week 1 - What to eat

- Eat as much white meat as you want. (If you are vegetarian you may have pulses instead of meat.)

- Eat as much fish as you want, including shellfish. (There are high levels of mercury in swordfish, tilefish and shark, so it's best to avoid these.)

- Eat as many vegetables, sprouted foods and fruits as you want (except for bananas – they aren't allowed during the first week).

- Eat herbs and spices – use them plentifully, they'll really bring your food to life.

- Have one fistful of nuts and seeds (milled flaxseeds are amazing) and one fistful of dried fruit a day. (N.B. Fistful, not handful.)

- Eggs are allowed.

- Vinegar. (With nothing else added.)

- Eat more vegetables than fruit, but eat as much fruit as you like.

That's it, nothing else! No dairy, alcohol, carbs, sugar, red meat, caffeine or anything packaged.

TOP TIPS FOR WEEK 1

- Apple cider vinegar is particularly good for detoxing. It's full of minerals, vitamins and enzymes, and is amazing for the immune system.

- Herbal teas and coconut water are good to drink.

- You can also have corn, sweet potato and other root vegetables, but no white potato this week.

- Drinks – herbal teas, coconut water, water, fresh juices. Drink 2–3 litres of water a day.

- Almond and cashew spreads are really yummy.

- I also find liquorice tea really good for calming my sweet tooth.

- Dried nori strips (seaweed) are a delicious snack and really nutritious. Eat as much as you like – it's a great alternative to crisps.

- If you have a sweet tooth go and buy some Nakd bars. They are really delicious and during the detox you are allowed all the flavours except cocoa – although this week you should also avoid the ones with added oats or soya. Also, make sure you deduct your Nakd bar from your daily allocation of one fistful of nuts/seeds and one fistful of dried fruit. One Nakd bar is equal to about half a fistful of both nuts/seeds and dried fruit, so two Nakd bars would be your daily quota.

Week 2 – What to eat

- Same as week 1, but add one fistful of carbs a day in the form of oats, couscous, brown rice, wholemeal pasta, potatoes, buckwheat, amaranth and quinoa – and go wheat-free for at least one day. (If you are sensitive to insulin spikes, avoid potatoes this week.)

- Plus two tablespoons of coconut oil or one tablespoon of olive oil.

- You may have olives, but count them as part of your olive oil quota, so ten olives are equal to one tablespoon of olive oil.

- You may have dried coconut slices, but have this as part of your dried fruit quota, and no added anything.

- Natural yogurt. (If you do not eat dairy, try other yogurts, but with no added nasties!)

- Bananas!

TOP TIP FOR WEEK 2

- I would really advise that you take spirulina, and / or psyllium husks, thirty minutes before you eat in the morning and thirty minutes before your afternoon snack. It will help with your digestion, fill you up and balance your blood sugar levels, so you are not tempted to eat out of tiredness. You can find these in health food shops.

And that's it!

Just one set of simple rules to follow over two weeks and you can make a huge difference to the rest of your life!

You are going to feel amazing!

Once you start to feel good in your process of detoxing, really fix this amazing feeling in your memory; do you want to feel this light, and even lighter, this energised and even more energised, fit, fitter and fittest? Or do you want to go about your day in a sludge, foggy, misty and exhausted!

By the end of the two weeks you will look and feel younger. One of the benefits of eating clean is that your skin, hair, nails and eyes all become bright and younger-looking. Your posture will improve, which instantly makes you look younger; your stomach will get a lot flatter, and we always associate small waistlines with youth, your flexibility will massively improve, which means you will walk with agility, and you will be bouncing off the walls with energy! I can't wait to help you to get there!

Meal Plans

CHAPTER 9

Meal Plans

I've provided some great recipes for you to help you to decide what to eat during the detox and also put together some meal plans that should let you see how you can combine them.

The following plans are provided:

- Summer
- Winter
- Vegetarian
- Fast Food/Quick Recipes

With any of these, if you want to switch meals around during a day, go ahead. There's no reason why you can't have the suggested lunch for supper instead – or for breakfast, for that matter, if that's what suits you!

If you swap meals between days, say Tuesday and Wednesday's lunches, for example, make sure you are still sticking to the detox guidelines over the course of that day. And remember also that while you can have any week 1 meal or snack in week 2, you can't always swap the other way round as week 2 is a little more relaxed. If you're compiling your own eating plan or tailoring one of those suggested here, just take a moment to double check.

The speedy meal planner deserves a special mention. Not everyone has time to do a lot of cooking and preparation – and not everyone wants to! What I've done with this is to write some recipes that don't take a lot of preparation or use components you can buy pre-prepared.

That actually applies to all the plans: if you want to buy your salads ready made or select them from a salad bar to save having to prepare them yourself, go ahead and do so – just stick to the vegetable choices and avoid anything slathered in mayonnaise.

You can buy your fruit and/or vegetables pre-prepared or frozen (although fresh is always far healthier, as once the fruit and vegetables are cut and packed they lose their nutrients) – just check the labels to make sure there are no added nasties, such as sugar. You can also buy cartons of fresh soups rather than making your own from scratch, but again, check the labels and remember you're more likely to get something suitable from the health food shop than the supermarket. Bear in mind you can make vegetable soup out of pretty much anything you have to hand – cooking some fresh vegetables with herbs and spices, then pureeing the mix in a blender, will make a tasty soup in a very short time. Follow it with some dried fruit, nuts and seeds (week 1) or enjoy it with some nut bread (week 2) to make a more substantial meal.

Nakd bars make handy snacks, as do nori strips. You can also replace any meal or snack with fruit (just make sure you eat more vegetables than fruit over the course of the day) or vegetables. Adding a salad or some chopped veggies (carrot sticks or cucumber spears, for example) to a favourite snack can turn it into a meal.

Make good use of herbs and spices, they really can make food zing! Spicy food can often feel more satisfying, so if you like a bit of heat in your food, there's no reason to deny yourself.

Plan ahead, too. You can make nut bread ahead of time and freeze it in slices, ready for when you need it. Vegetable chips for tomorrow's snack can be cooked while the oven is on for tonight's dinner, and most soups freeze well, so make a bigger batch when you have time and freeze it in portions.

It's all about making the detox as manageable as possible for you and maximising your chances of success. I know the benefits of following the detox are more than worth the changes that you'll be making in your shopping, cooking and eating habits, but I also know that habits take a while to change, so this can be challenging to undertake.

However, with a little help and planning you can do it - and you'll never look back!

Chapter 9 : Meal Plans   67

Summer Meal Plan

WEEK 1	Breakfast	Snack
Monday	Boiled Eggs & Carrot sticks pg 103	Nuts & Seeds
Tuesday	Pineapple & Mango Smoothie pg 96	Carrot & Celery Juice pg 88
Wednesday	Stuffed Portobello Mushrooms pg 124	Sweet Potato Cakes pg 156
Thursday	Lemon Infusion & Grapes pg 102	Romaine Parcels pg 154
Friday	Scrambled Eggs & Spring Onion pg 122	Apple & Cinnamon Crisps pg 136
Saturday	Fruity Omelette pg 108	Apple & Greens with Lime Juice pg 85
Sunday	Pineapple & Strawberry Smoothie pg 93	Nori Strips

Lunch	Snack	Dinner
Broccoli Soup pg 170	Blueberry Juice pg 87	Smoked Salmon Salad pg 220
Kelp Pot Noodle pg 190	Nakd Bar	Sea Bream & Vegetables pg 218
Hot Smoked Mackerel & Vegetable Medley pg 188	Apple & Raisins	Asparagus Frittata pg 164
Carrot & Leek Soup pg 172	Detox Energy Bars pg 142	Tuna Salad pg 238
Thai Prawn Soup pg 234	Easy Guacamole with Celery Sticks pg 144	Spicy Vegetable Stew pg 230
Thai Vegetable Soup pg 236	Fig Almond Truffles pg 146	Salmon Steaks & Green Salad pg 214
Asparagus Salad topped with Poached Eggs pg 166	Lemon, Apple, Ginger & Carrot Juice pg 92	Spicy Tomato & Vegtable Soup pg 228

Summer Meal Plan

WEEK 2	Breakfast	Snack
Monday	Quinoa Apple Porridge pg 116	Nuts & Seeds
Tuesday	Colourful Fruit Salad pg 104	Kale & Spinach Smoothie pg 94
Wednesday	Tarragon Mushrooms on Nut Bread pg 128	Green Vegetable Smoothie pg 90
Thursday	Fruit Salad with Nutmeg Yogurt Dressing pg 106	Carrot Batons & Nuts pg 140
Friday	Apple & Ginger Porridge pg 100	Celery & Beetroot Juice pg 91
Saturday	Fruit Salad & Yogurt with Almond Butter pg 112	Parsnip Crisps pg 148
Sunday	Savoury Breakfast Quinoa pg 118	Mint Yogurt Dip & Veg pg 150

Lunch	Snack	Dinner
Watercress Soup pg 242	Berry Blitz Smoothie pg 86	Vegetable Stew pg 240
Smoked Salmon on Nut Bread pg 126	Detox Energy Bar pg 142	Pasta & Tomato Sauce with Salad pg 206
Cauliflower Soup pg 174	Nori Strips	Mediterranean Roasted Vegetables pg 198
Quinoa Salad with Avocado & Strawberries pg 210	Apple & Cucumber Juice pg 84	Salmon Steaks & Green Salad pg 214
Courgette Noodles pg 180	Plantain Chips pg 152	Asparagus Frittata pg 164
Corn Chowder pg 178	Nakd Bar	Cod Steaks with Courgette & Tomato Bake pg 176
Scallops with Green Beans & Broccoli pg 216	Grilled Veg Kebabs with Nuts & Seeds pg 141	Baked Sweet Potato with Spicy Asian Coleslaw pg 168

Winter Meal Plan

WEEK 1	Breakfast	Snack
Monday	Pineapple & Mango Smoothie pg 96	Sweet Potato Cakes pg 156
Tuesday	Stuffed Portobello Mushrooms pg 124	Apple & Cinnamon Crisps pg 136
Wednesday	Boiled Eggs & Carrot Sticks pg 103	Carrot & Celery Juice pg 88
Thursday	Scrambled Eggs & Spring Onion pg 122	Nori Strips
Friday	Lemon Infusion & Grapes pg 102	Romaine Parcels pg 154
Saturday	Poached Eggs & Portobello Mushrooms pg 114	Apple & Greens with Lime Juice pg 85
Sunday	Fruity Omelette pg 108	Blueberry Juice pg 87

Lunch	Snack	Dinner
Asparagus Salad topped with Poached Eggs pg 166	Easy Guacamole with Celery Sticks pg 144	Sweet Potato with Roasted Vegetables pg 232
Broccoli Soup pg 170	Detox Energy Bars pg 142	Root Vegetable Soup pg 212
Carrot & Leek Soup pg 172	Apple & Raisins	Sea Bream & Vegetables pg 218
Thai Prawn Soup pg 234	Nuts & Seeds	Asparagus Frittata pg 164
Tuna Salad pg 238	Apple & Cucumber Juice pg 84	Spicy Tomato & Vegtable Soup pg 228
Thai Vegetable Soup pg 236	Lemon, Apple, Ginger & Carrot Juice pg 92	Salmon Steaks & Green Salad pg 214
Kelp Pot Noodle pg 190	Fig Almond Truffles pg 146	Hot Smoked Mackerel & Vegetable Medley pg 188

Winter Meal Plan

WEEK 2	Breakfast	Snack
Monday	Tarragon Mushrooms on Nut Bread pg 128	Nori Strips
Tuesday	Smoked Salmon on Nut Bread pg 126	Sweet Potato Cakes pg 156
Wednesday	Quinoa Apple Porridge pg 116	Plantain Chips pg 152
Thursday	Scrambled Egg & Cherry Tomatoes on Nut Bread pg 120	Celery & Beetroot Juice 91
Friday	Fruit Salad with Nutmeg Yogurt Dressing pg 106	Nuts & Seeds
Saturday	Healthy Vegetable Hash pg 110	Parsnip Crisps pg 148
Sunday	Savoury Breakfast Quinoa pg 118	Green Vegetable Smoothie pg 90

The Body Rescue Detox Recipe Book

Lunch	Snack	Dinner
Courgette Noodles pg 180	Tomato, Pepper & Cucumber Juice pg 97	Minestrone Soup pg 200
Garlic Prawns with Spaghetti pg 184	Kale & Spinach Smoothie pg 94	Spicy Vegetable Stew pg 230
Corn Chowder pg 178	Detox Energy Bar pg 142	Mediterranean Roasted Vegetables pg 198
Speedy Stir-Fry pg 222	Celeriac Chips pg 138	Vegetable Stew pg 240
Baked Sweet Potato with Spicy Asian Coleslaw pg 168	Grilled Veg Kebabs pg 141	Pasta & Tomato Sauce with Salad pg 206
Cauliflower Soup 174	Mint Yogurt Dip & Vegetables pg 150	Egg Fried Rice pg 182
Scallops with Green Beans & Broccoli pg 216	Apple & Raisins	Spicy Parsnip Soup pg 224

Vegetarian Meal Plan

WEEK 1	Breakfast	Snack
Monday	Scrambled Eggs and Spring Onionpg pg 122	Nuts & Seeds
Tuesday	Pineapple & Strawberry Smoothie pg 93	Apple & Greens with Lime Juice pg 85
Wednesday	Poached Eggs & Portobello Mushrooms pg 114	Apple & Cinnamon Crisps pg 136
Thursday	Pineapple & Mango Smoothie pg 96	Sweet Potato Cakes pg 156
Friday	Boiled Eggs & Carrot Sticks pg 103	Romaine Parcels pg 154
Saturday	Stuffed Portobello Mushrooms pg 124	Carrot & Celery Juice pg 88
Sunday	Lemon Infusion & Grapes pg 102	Nori Strips

Lunch	Snack	Dinner
Broccoli Soup pg 170	Blueberry Juice pg 87	Sweet Potato with Roasted Vegetables pg 232
Lentil & Red Pepper Soup pg 192	Easy Guacamole with Celery Sticks 144	Asparagus Frittata pg 164
Carrot & Leek Soup pg 172	Apple & Cucumber Juice pg 84	Spicy Vegetable Stew pg 230
Asparagus Salad topped with Poached Eggs pg 166	Lemon, Apple, Ginger & Carrot Juice pg 92	Lentil & Vegetable Soup pg 196
Kelp Pot Noodle pg 190	Detox Energy Bar pg 142	Root Vegetable Stew pg 212
Thai Vegetable Soup pg 236	Tomato, Pepper & Cucumber Juice pg 97	Sweet Potato with Roasted Vegetables pg 232
Large mixed Salad with two Boiled Eggs	Fig Almond Truffles pg 146	Spicy Tomato & Vegetable Soup pg 228

Vegetarian Meal Plan

WEEK 2	Breakfast	Snack
Monday	Berry Blitz Smoothie pg 86	Celeriac Chips pg 138
Tuesday	Quinoa Apple Porridge pg 116	Kale & Spinach Smoothie pg 94
Wednesday	Apple & Ginger Porridge pg 100	Nuts & Seeds
Thursday	Fruity Omelette pg 108	Nakd Bar
Friday	Healthy Vegetable Hash pg 110	Celery & Beetroot Juice pg 91
Saturday	Tarragon Mushrooms on Nut Bread pg 128	Green Vegetable Smoothie pg 90
Sunday	Yogurt with Fruit, Nuts & Seeds pg 130	Nori Strips

Lunch	Snack	Dinner
Carrot & Leek Soup pg 172	Detox Energy Bar pg 142	Pasta & Tomato Sauce with Salad pg 206
Cauliflower Soup pg 174	Plantain Chips pg 152	Vegetable Stew pg 240
Baked Sweet Potato with Spicy Asian Coleslaw pg 168	Tomato, Pepper & Cucumber Juice pg 97	Spicy Parsnip Soup pg 224
Minestrone Soup pg 200	Mint Yogurt Dip & Vegetables pg 150	Mediterranean Roasted Vegetables pg 198
Corn Chowder pg 178	Apple & Raisins	Courgette Noodles pg 180
Quinoa Salad with Avocado & Strawberries pg 210	Parsnip Crisps pg 148	Lentil & Vegetable Soup pg 196
Watercress Soup pg 242	Grilled Veg Kebabs pg 141	Egg Fried Rice pg 182

Fast Food/ Quick Recipes Meal Plan

WEEK 1	Breakfast	Snack
Monday	Lemon Infusion & Grapes pg 102	Green Vegetbale Smoothie 90
Tuesday	Boiled Eggs & Carrot Sticks pg 103	Apple & Greens with Lime Juice pg 85
Wednesday	Pineapple & Mango Smoothie pg 96	Nori Strips
Thursday	Fruity Omelette pg 108	Apple & Cinnamon Crisps pg 136
Friday	Pineapple & Strawberry Smoothie pg 93	Carrot & Celery Juice pg 88
Saturday	Scrambled Eggs & Spring Onion pg 122	Blueberry Juice pg 87
Sunday	Stuffed Portobello Mushrooms pg 124	Romaine Parcels pg 154

Lunch	Snack	Dinner
Tuna Salad pg 238	Detox Energy Bar pg 142	Root Vegetable Soup pg 212
Spicy Tomato & Vegetable Soup pg 228	Nuts & Seeds	Sea Bream & Vegetables pg 218
Broccoli Soup pg 170	Nakd Bar	Asparagus Frittata pg 164
Smoked Salmon Salad pg 220	Lemon, Apple Ginger & Carrot Juice pg 92	Spicy Vegetable Stew pg 230
Thai Vegetable Soup pg 236	Easy Guacamole with Celery Sticks pg 144	Hot Smoked Mackerel & Vegetable Medley pg 188
Tuna Salad pg 238	Apple & Raisins	Carrot & Leek Soup pg 172
Asparagus Salad topped with Poached Eggs pg 166	Fig Almond Truffles pg 146	Salmon Steaks & Green Salad pg 214

Fast Food/ Quick Recipes Meal Plan

WEEK 2	Breakfast	Snack
Monday	Savoury Breakfast Quinoa pg 118	Nori Strips
Tuesday	Fruity Omelette pg 108	Grilled Veg Kebabs pg 141
Wednesday	Boiled Eggs & Carrot Sticks pg 103	Celery & Beetroot Juice pg 91
Thursday	Tarragon Mushrooms on Nut Bread pg 128	Berry Blitz Smoothie pg 86
Friday	Yogurt with Fruit, Nuts & Seeds pg 130	Plantain Chips pg 152
Saturday	Apple & Ginger Porridge pg 100	Carrot Batons & Nuts pg 140
Sunday	Poached Eggs & Portobello Mushrooms pg 114	Nori Strips

Lunch	Snack	Dinner
Minestrone Soup pg 200	Apple & Raisins	Speedy Stir-Fry pg 222
Corn Chowder pg 178	Kale & Spinach Smoothie pg 94	Vegetable Stew pg 240
Cauliflower Soup pg 174	Parsnip Crisps pg 148	Garlic Prawns with Spaghetti pg 184
Smoked Salmon & Shop-Bought Salad pg 226	Fruit Salad & Yogurt with Almond Nut Butter pg 112	Spicy Parsnip Soup pg 224
Quinoa Salad pg 208	Apple & Cucumber Juice pg 84	Halibut & Fennel Salad pg 186
Scallops with Green Beans & Broccoli pg 216	Nakd Bar	Pasta & Tomato Sauce with Salad pg 206
Quinoa Salad with Avocado & Strawberries pg 210	Tomato, Pepper & Cucumber Juice pg 97	Mediterranean Roasted Vegetables pg 198

RECIPES:
Smoothies & Juices

CHAPTER 10a

Apple & Cucumber
JUICE

Ingredients

- 2 apples
- 1/2 cucumber
- 1 stick celery
- 1 handful of spinach
- 1 handful of watercress
- Small piece root ginger

Serves

Method

1. Juice all ingredients; add ice or water, as required.

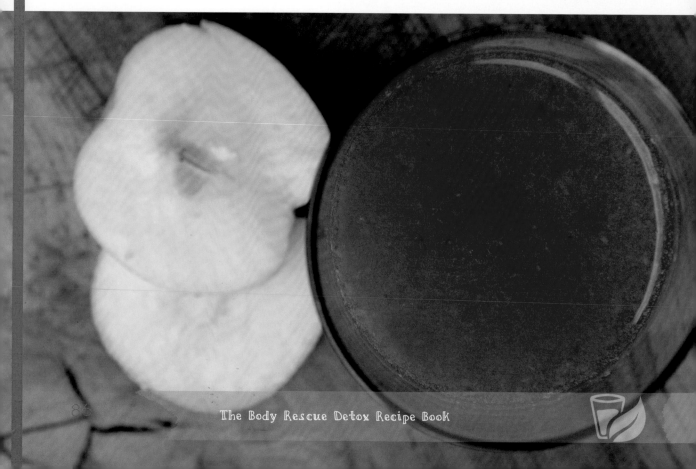

Apple & Greens with Lime JUICE

Serves 1

Ingredients

- 2 apples
- 1/2 cucumber
- 1 stick celery
- 1 handful of kale
- 1tsp lime juice

Method

1 Pass all ingredients through a juicer, stir in the lime juice, and enjoy!

Watch how to make this here!
http://www.thebodyrescueplan.com/apple-and-limes-juice/

Berry Blitz
SMOOTHIE

Serves

Ingredients

- Handful raspberries
- Handful blackberries
- 7fl oz / 200mls natural yogurt
- ½ tsp cinnamon
- 1 tsp coconut oil
- 4 / 5 ice cubes

Method

1 Blitz all ingredients in a blender until smooth, then enjoy!

Blueberry
JUICE

Serves 1

Ingredients

- 1 turnip
- 1/2 green pepper
- 2 apples
- 1 handful blueberries

Method

1 Pass all ingredients through a juicer and serve!

Did you know?

1 cup of blueberries a day could help prevent heart disease.

Carrot & Celery
JUICE

Serves  1

Ingredients

- 1 handful of kale
- 1 handful of watercress
- 1/3 cucumber
- 3 stalks of celery
- 1 carrot
- 1cm piece of ginger
- Juice of 1/2 a lemon

Method

1 Pass all ingredients through a juicer, stir in the lemon juice, and enjoy!

Green Veg
SMOOTHIE

Ingredients

- 1 handful kale
- 1 head broccoli
- 1/4 cucumber
- 1 stick celery
- 1/2 tsp ground ginger
- 1 tsp lemon juice
- 6fl oz / 170mls water

Serves

Method

1 Whizz all ingredients in a blender until smooth; add more water if necessary to get the consistency you want, then enjoy!

Celery & Beetroot

JUICE

Ingredients

- 2 apples
- 1/2 cucumber
- 1 stick celery
- 1 handful of kale
- 1tsp lime juice

Serves

Method

1 Pass all ingredients through a juicer, stir in the lime juice, and enjoy!

Lemon, Apple, Ginger & Carrot
JUICE

Serves  1

Ingredients

- 2 apples
- 2 carrots
- 1/2 lemon
- 1 x 1 inch piece fresh ginger

Method

1 Process all ingredients through a vegetable juicer and enjoy

Pineapple & Strawberry
SMOOTHIE

WEEK 1 & 2

Ingredients

- 1/2 a pineapple
- Handful of strawberries

Serves 1

Method

1 Place fruit in a blender and process for a yummy morning smoothie!

Kale & Spinach SMOOTHIE

Serves 1

Ingredients

- 1 frozen banana
- $1/4$ avocado
- 1 handful kale
- 1 handful spinach
- 8fl oz / 227mls / 1 cup water
- 1tsp milled flaxseeds

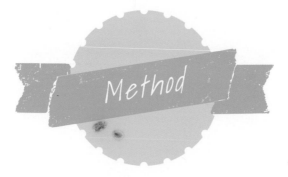

Method

1 Blend thoroughly, then drink immediately!

Pineapple & Mango
SMOOTHIE

Serves  1

Ingredients

- 1/2 a mango
- 1/2 a pineapple

Method

1 Place fruit in a blender and process for a simple and delicious morning smoothie!

Tomato, Pepper & Cucumber

JUICE

Serves  1 2

Ingredients

- 1 large tomato, cored & chopped
- 1/4 English cucumber, peeled & chopped
- 1/4 red pepper, seeded & chopped
- Few leaves of mint
- 1 tsp lemon juice

Method

1 Puree all ingredients in a blender until smooth; add ice or water, as required!

RECIPES:

Breakfasts

CHAPTER 10b

Apple & Ginger

PORRIDGE

Serves

Ingredients

- 2¹/₂ oz / 75g/ ³/₄ cup porridge oats
- 18fl oz / 500mls / 2 cups water
- 1 large eating apple
- Ground ginger

Method

1 Cook the porridge oats in the water.

2 Peel, core and chop the apple. Put in a plan with just enough water to cover and cook until soft, then drain off the water

3 Serve the porridge topped with the warm cooked apple and sprinkled with ground ginger.

Lemon Infusion & Grapes

Ingredients

- A slice of lemon
- 1 small bunch grapes

Method

Serves

1

1. Add the lemon slice to a mug of hot water, eat the grapes, and enjoy!

Boiled Eggs & Carrot Sticks

Ingredients

- 2 eggs
- 1 carrot, cut into batons

Method

 Serves

1 Boil the eggs and use carrot sticks instead of toast soldiers. Delicious!

COLOURFUL Fruit Salad & Yogurt

Serves 1

Ingredients

- 2 kiwi fruit
- 6-8 strawberries
- Greek yogurt
- Chopped nuts (optional)

Method

1. Peel and slice the kiwi fruit.

2. Hull and slice the strawberries.

3. Mix together in a bowl and top with the Greek yogurt. If liked, sprinkle with chopped nuts.

Fruit Salad with Nutmeg Yogurt

DRESSING

Ingredients

Serves

- 1 medium ripe pear, diced
- 1 medium apple, diced
- 4oz / 115g / 1/2 cup red seedless grapes, halved
- 4oz / 115g / 1/2 cup green seedless grapes, halved
- 1 tbsp lemon juice
- 4 tbsps natural yogurt
- Few drops vanilla extract
- 1/2 tsp ground nutmeg
- Cinnamon

Method

1 Place the prepared pears, apples, and grapes in a large bowl with the lemon juice and toss gently to combine. Drain off the juice.

2 Stir the vanilla and nutmeg cinnamon into the yogurt and add it to the fruit. Toss gently until fruit is coated.

3 Serve in bowls, sprinkled with cinnamon.

Fruity Omelette

Serves  1

Ingredients

- 2 eggs
- 1/2 tsp cinnamon
- A fistful dried fruit

Method

1 Beat the eggs with the cinnamon. Heat a non-stick frying pan and pour in the egg mixture, swirling to evenly cover the base. Cook for a few minutes until set and golden underneath.

2 Sprinkle the dried fruit on the top, then put under the grill for a short time to set the top.

3 Fold over (or roll up) and serve!

HEALTHY Vegetable Hash

Ingredients  Serves ①②

- 1 tbsp coconut oil
- 1 shallot, finely chopped
- 6oz / 170g / 3/4 cup chestnut mushrooms, chopped
- 1 red pepper, chopped
- 6oz / 170g / 3/4 cup baby sweetcorn, halved lengthways
- 1/4 tsp dried sage
- Salt and freshly ground black pepper

Method

1 Melt the coconut oil in a saucepan and fry the shallot for 2-3 minutes.

2 Add the rest of the vegetables and cook gently, stirring occasionally.

3 When the vegetables are cooked, season and serve immediately!

Fruit Salad & Yogurt with Almond Nut Butter

Serves

Ingredients

- 1 pot prepared chopped fruit (most supermarkets offer these in the fresh fruit section)
- 1 small pot natural yogurt
- 1 tbsp almond nut butter

Method

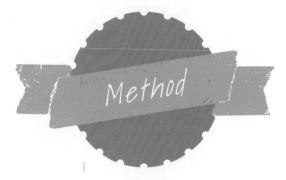

1 Combine and enjoy!

POACHED EGGS
& Portobello Mushrooms

Serves 1 2

Ingredients

- 4 portobello mushrooms, stems removed & wiped
- 4 eggs
- Salt and freshly ground black pepper

Method

1 Preheat the oven to 200°C / 390°F / gas mark 6 and line a baking sheet with baking paper.

2 Place the mushrooms, gills side up, onto the paper. Bake for around 20 minutes, until tender. They may release water as they cook, so if necessary pat with kitchen paper before you put them on the plate.

3 Poach the eggs, timing them to be ready at the same time as the mushrooms. Serve the mushrooms with the eggs inside, seasoned with salt and pepper.

Quinoa Apple PORRIDGE

Serves

Ingredients

- 8oz / 225g / 1 cup uncooked quinoa, soaked in water overnight
- 3 eating apples
- 1 tsp ground mixed spice

Method

Handy Tip!

If you make this when you are not on a detox, you can add 2 tsps of honey!

1 Peel, core and chop the apples. Put them in a saucepan with enough water to just cover them. Bring to the boil then simmer for about 15 minutes, or until tender. Drain, then mash, or puree with a hand blender.

2 Drain the quinoa and put it in a saucepan with 3/4 pint / 415mls / 1 3/4 cups water. Bring the mixture to a boil, then cover and lower the heat. Allow to cook for 15 minutes, or until all of the liquid has been absorbed.

3 Stir in the pureed apple and mixed spice, and serve!

SAVOURY
Breakfast Quinoa

Serves

Ingredients

- 4oz / 115g / ½ cup quinoa
- 2 tsps coconut oil
- 6 mushrooms, quartered
- 1 yellow pepper, chopped
- 1 large handful roughly chopped spinach
- Salt and freshly ground black pepper

Method

1 Cook the quinoa according to the instructions.

2 Heat the coconut oil in a pan and cook the peppers and mushrooms. When they are done, stir in the quinoa.

3 Add the spinach and allow to wilt.

4 Season to taste and serve!

SCRAMBLED
Egg & Cherry Tomatoes
ON NUT BREAD

Serves  **1**

Ingredients

- 1 egg
- Salt and freshly ground black pepper
- 4 cherry tomatoes, quartered
- 1/2 tsp basil
- 1 slice The Body Rescue Nut Bread

Method

1. Beat the egg and season with salt and pepper.

2. Heat a non-stick pan and add the egg, the cherry tomatoes and the basil. Cook, stirring, until the egg is scrambled and the tomatoes are cooked.

3. Toast the nut bread and pile the eggs and tomatoes on top to serve!

Scrambled Eggs & Spring Onion

Serves

Ingredients

- 2 eggs
- 1 spring onion, chopped
- Salt and freshly ground black pepper

Method

1 Crack the eggs into a non-stick pan. Allow the whites to just begin to set, then break the yolks and stir together.

2 add the chopped spring onion to the pan and stir through.

3 Season with salt and pepper and serve when the eggs are cooked.

STUFFED
Portobello
Mushrooms

Serves

Ingredients

- 1 red onion, chopped
- 2 cloves garlic, crushed
- 8 cherry tomatoes
- 8 olives, sliced (If making this for detox week 1, omit the olives)
- 4 large portobello mushrooms, stems removed and chopped

Method

1 Dry fry the onion in a non-stick pan until it begins to soften. Add the garlic, tomatoes and chopped mushroom stems and cook for another 2-3 minutes. Add the olives and stir into the mix.

2 Preheat the oven to 200°C / 390°F / gas mark 6 and cover a baking tray with parchment paper.

3 Put the mushrooms, gills side up, on the tray and divide the cooked vegetables between them.

4 Bake in the oven for 10-12 minutes, until the mushrooms are cooked!

Watch how to make this here!
http://www.thebodyrescueplan.com/stuffed-portobello-mushrooms/

Smoked Salmon on Nut Bread

Serves

Ingredients

- 4oz / 115g / 1/2 cup smoked salmon
- 1 tsp lime juice
- 1 slice The Body Rescue Nut Bread
  Salt and freshly ground black pepper

Method

1 Cut the smoked salmon slices into strips and sprinkle with the lemon juice.

2 Pile onto the nut bread and season with salt and freshly ground black pepper.

Tarragon Mushrooms on Nut Bread

Serves 1

Ingredients

- 1 tsp olive oil
- 4 chestnut mushrooms, sliced
- 1 tsp dried tarragon
- 1 slice The Body Rescue Nut Bread

Method

1 Heat the olive oil in a pan and add the sliced mushrooms. Sauté until almost cooked, then add the tarragon and mix thoroughly. Continue to cook until mushrooms are tender.

2 Toast the nut bread and pile the herby mushrooms on top to serve!

YOGURT
with Fruit, Nuts & Seeds

Serves 1

Ingredients

- 1 small pot natural yogurt
- Dried fruit, nuts and seeds from daily allowance

Method

1. Mix together and enjoy!

Muesli

Ingredients

- 4¹/₂oz / 128g / 1¹/₂ cups oats
- 3¹/₂oz / 90g / 1/₂ cup chopped dates
- 3¹/₂oz / 90g / 1/₂ cup chopped walnuts & pecans
- 1¹/₂oz / 40g / 1/₄ cup milled flax seeds
- 1¹/₂oz / 40g / 1/₄ cup sunflower seeds
- 2¹/₂oz / 75g / 1/₄ cup raisins
- 2 tbsp coconut oil
- Plain yogurt or fromage frais

Did you know? Milled flax seeds are high in omega 3 which have been proven to help you lose weight!

Method

1 Melt the coconut oil in a wok or frying pan.

2 Place all the ingredients into the pan and cook, stirring continually, for 6 minutes.

3 Store your muesli in an airtight container.

4 Serve a handful on some plain yogurt or fromage frais.

RECIPES:
Snacks
CHAPTER 10c

Apple & Cinnamon CRISPS

Ingredients

- 2 eating apples (Braeburn or Granny Smiths work well for this)
- Cinnamon

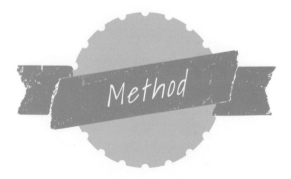

Method

1 Preheat the oven to 150°C / 300°F / gas mark 2 and line a baking sheet with baking paper.

2 Core the apples and slice very thinly to make apple rings. Dust with cinnamon and arrange on the baking sheet. Put in the oven for 50–60 minutes. After 25 minutes turn the apple slices over. They're ready when they're dried, light and golden in colour.

3 When cool, store in an airtight container! If any slices turn brown, discard them.

Celeriac Chips

Ingredients

- Celeriac
- Paprika
- Chilli

Did you know?

B vitamins must be present for about 100 other enzymes to work efficiently, and Paprika has 4% of the recommended daily intake of vitamin B6!!!

Method

1 Cut celeriac into bite size crisps, put on an oven tray and sprinkle with paprika, and chilli if you like it hot! In week 2 you can also cover with coconut oil, which is divine!

2 Cook on 190°C / 375°F / gas mark 5 for about 30-40 minutes.

Carrot Batons & Nuts

Serves   1

Ingredients

- Handful of carrot batons (bought pre-prepared)
- Nuts from your allowance

Method

1 This is a lovely combination of foods – eat and enjoy!

Grilled Veg Kebabs

Ingredients

- 6 cherry tomatoes
- 6 button mushrooms
- 1/2 green pepper, cut into chunks
- 1/2 tbsp olive oil

Method

1 Thread the veg onto 2 metal skewers and brush with olive oil.

2 Grill until soft and serve!

DETOX
Energy Bars

Ingredients

- 4oz / 115g/ 1/2 cup almonds
- 4oz / 115g/ 1/2 cup dates
- 1 tsp maca powder
- 1 tbsp chia seeds
- 4oz / 115g / 1/2 cup dried apricots
- 4oz / 115g / 1/2 cup cashew nuts
- 8oz / 225g / 1 cup raisins
- 1 tsp vanilla extract
- 1 tsp cinnamon

Did you know?
These are yummy soft or hard! When you take the paste out of the blender it is more like fudge and when you freeze them they become more like toffee!

Method

1 Blend all ingredients in a blender.

2 Take out the mixture and place on cellophane, then flatten it out.

3 Place more cellophane on top and place in the freezer for 30 minutes or so.

4 Take out and cut up into squares, all ready to eat!

EASY
Guacamole
with Celery Sticks

Ingredients

for the Guacamole

- 1 large avocado
- 1/2 tsp dried cumin
- 1/2 tsp smoked paprika
- 1/2 tsp dried oregano
- Pinch cayenne pepper

Ingredients

to Serve

- Celery stalks

Serves

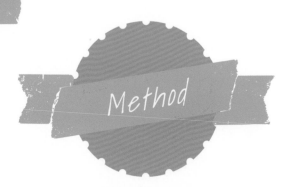

1 2

Method

1 Halve the avocado, remove the stone and scoop out the flesh.

2 Mash the flesh with the seasonings and whisk with a fork until creamy.

3 Serve immediately with the celery stalks!

Fig Almond Truffles

Ingredients

- 2 1/4 oz / 68g / 1/4 cup almonds
- 7oz / 200g / scant 1 cup dried figs
- 4 1/2 oz / 130g / 1/2 cup Medjool dates
- 4 1/2 oz / 130g / 1/2 cup dried figs, stemmed and chopped
- 3 tbsp fresh orange juice
- 1/4 tsp vanilla seeds
- 1 tsp ground cinnamon

Method

1 Place the almonds in a food processor and blend until finely chopped, but not ground totally smooth.

2 Add to the rest of the ingredients and mix thoroughly.

3 Roll into balls and serve!

Parsnip Crisps

Ingredients

- 1¼lbs / 600g / 2½ cups parsnips
- 2 tbsp coconut oil

Did you know?

Root vegetables make delicious crisps and chips! They are high in vitamin C, vitamin B-6, thiamin and pantothenic acid, as well as vitamin K and vitamin E!

Method

1 Preheat the oven to 180°C / 350°F / gas mark 4.

2 Grate the parsnips with a peeler.

3 Melt the coconut oil in a pan and drizzle over the parsnips in an ovenproof dish.

4 Cook for 25 minutes.

5 Allow to cool then eat as a snack on its own, or drizzle with vinegar or a nice tomato salsa!

Mint Yogurt dip with Vegetables

Ingredients
for the Mint Yogurt Dip

- 4 sprigs of fresh mint
- Juice of 1 lemon
- ¼ tsp garlic powder
- 6oz / 170g / ¾ cup natural yogurt
- Sea and freshly ground black pepper

Serves
1 2

Ingredients
to Serve

A selection of vegetables e.g:
- cucumber
- carrots
- celery
- peppers

Method

1 Discard the stalks and chop the mint leaves very finely. Add to the yogurt.

2 Add the lemon juice and garlic powder, and season with salt and pepper. Mix thoroughly.

3 Serve with the vegetables!

Plantain CHIPS

Ingredients

- 1 pound plantains or green bananas.
- 1fl oz / 30ml coconut oil
- Coarse sea salt and ground pepper

Method

1 Preheat oven to 180°C / 350°F / gas mark 4. and line a baking sheet with parchment paper.

2 Peel and slice the plantains or green bananas thinly on the diagonal.

3 Toss the plantain slices in the oil, then arrange in a single layer on the baking sheet. Season with salt and pepper.

4 Bake for around 30 minutes until crisp and golden, turning the chips halfway through the cooking time.

5 Drain on kitchen paper. When cooled store in an airtight container, for a couple of days.

Romaine Parcels

Serves 1 2

Ingredients

- 1 large avocado
- 1 beef tomato, chopped
- ½ cucumber, chopped
- 1 tsp lemon juice
- 1 head romaine lettuce

Method

1 Halve the avocado, remove the stone and scoop out the flesh into a bowl. Mash the flesh thoroughly.

2 Add the tomato, cucumber and lemon juice, and combine thoroughly.

3 Put a spoonful of the mixture into a lettuce leaf and roll up to eat. Delicious!

Sweet Potato Cakes

Ingredients

- 2 sweet potatoes, cooked and peeled
- 10 dates
- 1 tsp cinnamon
- 1 tsp nutmeg
- 1 tbsp ground almonds
- 1 handful of raisins
- 1 egg

Did you know?

This is a delicious cake to have on a detox, and nice for breakfast too!

Method

1 Preheat oven to 200°C / 390°F / gas mark 6.

2 Blend all of the ingredients together in a blender; mould the mixture into cake shapes and place on a brownie/cookie baking tray.

3 Bake for 20-30 minutes!

Banana & Sultana
OAT COOKIES

Makes 6 Cookies!

Ingredients

- 1 large (or 2 small) apples (e.g. Braeburn)
- 1tsp lemon juice
- 1 large, ripe banana, mashed
- 4$1/_2$oz / 128g / 1$1/_2$ cups oats
- 1 tsp mixed spice
- 3$1/_2$oz / 90g / $1/_2$ cup sultanas

This is a flexible recipe, so if you'd rather use a different fruit, such as chopped apricots, or you'd like to add some chopped nuts, go ahead! You could also use nutmeg or ginger (for example) instead of mixed spice!

Method

1 Core, peel and chop the apples. Place in a saucepan with the lemon juice and cook over a low heat until soft (5-6 minutes). Allow to cool, then mash.

2 Put all of the ingredients in a bowl and mix thoroughly.

3 Preheat the oven to 180°C / 350°F / gas mark 4 and line a baking sheet with baking parchment.

4 Drop the mixture on to the parchment in cookie-sized portions; bake for 15-20 minutes.

Beetroot Chips & Curried Yogurt

Ingredients

- 4 beetroots
- Olive oil
- Salt
- Dried rosemary
- 2 tbsps plain low-fat Greek yogurt
- 1/4 tsp curry powder

Method

1 Preheat oven to 190°C / 375°F / gas mark 5.

2 Thinly slice beetroots. Divide between two baking sheets and spray or very lightly drizzle with olive oil. Add a pinch of salt and the rosemary.

3 Bake for 15-20 minutes or until crispy and slightly brown. Allow to cool.

4 Mix together the Greek yogurt and curry powder. Serve with beetroot chips and enjoy!

RECIPES:
Lunch & Supper Dishes

CHAPTER 10d

Asparagus Frittata

Ingredients

Serves

- 1 red onion, chopped
- 1 parsnip, chopped
- Handful of kale, chopped
- 10 asparagus spears
- 6 eggs, beaten and seasoned with salt and pepper
- Handful of parsley, chopped

Method

1 Dry fry parsnip and red onion in a large frying pan for a few minutes, then add kale and asparagus and cook for another minute.

2 Add the parsley to the egg mixture, pour into the pan and cook on a high heat for 1 minute. Using a spatula, slightly lift around the edges to allow some of the uncooked mixture to run under the sides. Cook for another 5 minutes or until the frittata is set around the edges but still soft in the middle.

3 Remove from the heat and allow the frittata to stand for 5 minutes in the pan.

4 Serve with a crunchy salad.

Asparagus Salad
TOPPED WITH Poached Eggs

Ingredients

Serves

- 2 bunches asparagus, trimmed
- 4 large eggs
- 2 bags rocket

Ingredients
for the Dressing

- 4 tbsps lemon juice
- Zest of 1/2 a lemon
- 1/2 tsp garlic powder
- Salt and freshly ground pepper

Method

1 Steam the asparagus until tender.

2 Poach the eggs, and drain.

3 Meanwhile, whisk the ingredients for the dressing in a large bowl. Set aside 4 tsps.

4 Toss the rocket with the dressing and divide the salad between 4 plates. Top with asparagus and a poached egg and drizzle with 1 tsp of the reserved dressing!

Baked Sweet Potato WITH SPICY Asian Coleslaw

Ingredients

- 4 large sweet potatoes
- 1/4 of a medium white cabbage, shredded
- 1/4 of a medium red cabbage, shredded
- 2 large carrots, grated
- 3oz / 85g / 1 cup bean sprouts
- 4 spring onions, sliced finely at an angle

Serves

Ingredients
for the Dressing

- 3/4 pint / 425mls natural yogurt
- 1/2 tsp grated ginger
- 2 tbsps water
- Pinch of himalayan salt

Method

1 Scrub the sweet potatoes, prick several times with a fork, and bake in the oven at 200°C / 390°F / gas mark 6 for about an hour, or until cooked.

2 To make the coleslaw, first thoroughly combine all the prepared vegetables in a bowl.

3 To make the dressing, mix all the ingredients together in a separate bowl.

4 Add the dressing to the salad and mix thoroughly.

5 Cut a cross into the potato and open up the cavity. Pile in the coleslaw and enjoy!

Broccoli Soup

Serves 1 2 3 4

Ingredients

- 2 onions
- 2 heads broccoli
- 10 asparagus spears
- 1/2 a bag of spinach
- 1 1/2 pints / 1L vegetable stock

Did you know?

If you have a Vitamix blender, simply blend all the ingredients for a hot, yummy nutritious soup!

Method

1 Dry fry the onion whilst steaming the broccoli and asparagus for 5 minutes or so.

2 Place all ingredients in a pan with vegetable stock.

3 Once cooked, process soup in a blender, then reheat as necessary for a hearty warm soup. This soup is really creamy and very delicious!

Carrot & Leek
SOUP

Serves 1 2 3 4

Ingredients

- 2¹/₂ pints / 1.4 litres / 6 cups vegetable stock
- 2lbs / 1kg / 4 cups carrots, sliced
- 2 large leeks, chopped
- 1 medium onion, chopped
- 2 stalks celery, chopped
- 3 tsps dried mixed herbs
- Chopped chives

Method

1 In a large pan, bring the vegetable stock to the boil and add all ingredients. Simmer for 20 minutes or until vegetables are tender.

2 Puree, reheat as necessary and serve garnished with chopped chives!

Cauliflower
SOUP

Ingredients

Serves 1 2 3 4

- 2 tbsps olive oil
- 2 shallots, chopped
- 4 spring onions, chopped
- 1 clove garlic, crushed
- 2 stalks celery, chopped
- 2 medium cauliflowers, broken into florets
- 1 tsp dried basil
- $\frac{1}{2}$ tsp dried marjoram
- $\frac{1}{2}$ tsp dried sage
- Salt and freshly ground black pepper
- $2\frac{1}{2}$ pints / 1.4 litres / 6 cups vegetable stock

Method

1 Heat the oil in a large pan and cook the shallots and spring onions for 2 minutes.

2 Add the garlic and celery and cook for another 2 minutes.

3 Add the cauliflower and seasonings and cook for 3-4 minutes.

4 Add the vegetable stock and bring to the boil. Simmer for around 15 minutes until the cauliflower is tender.

5 Blend until smooth, then reheat and serve!

COD STEAKS
WITH
Courgette & Tomato Bake

Ingredients

Serves

- 2 cod steaks, approx. 1 inch thick, 6oz / 170g
- 1 tbsp lemon juice
- 1/2 tbsp olive oil
- 1/2 tsp dried thyme
- 2 large courgettes, sliced
- 1 can or carton (15oz / 400g) of chopped tomatoes
- 1/2 tsp dried basil
- Salt and pepper to taste

> If making this when not on a detox, you can add cheese if you like! When the courgettes have been in 20 minutes (about 5 minutes before fish is ready) remove from oven, scatter grated cheese over the top and grill until the cheese bubbles!

Method

1 Preheat the oven to 200°C / 390°F / gas mark 6.

2 Pour the chopped tomatoes into an ovenproof dish. Add basil and season with salt and pepper.

3 Stir in the courgettes, cover with the tomatoes.

4 Bake in the oven for 20 minutes, or until courgettes are cooked.

5 As soon as the courgettes are in the oven, prepare the fish. Cut a piece of kitchen foil large enough to wrap the cod steaks and place it on a baking tray. Lightly oil the foil, then place the fish on it and sprinkle with the lemon juice, thyme, salt and pepper. Close up the foil parcel and place in the oven.

6 Bake in the oven for 20 minutes, or until fish is cooked, then serve with the vegetables!

Corn Chowder

Serves

1 2 3 4

Ingredients

- 2$^1/_2$ pints / 1.4 litres / 6 cups vegetable stock
- 1$^1/_2$lbs / 700g / 3 cups potatoes, peeled and chopped
- 1 onion, chopped
- 2 cloves garlic, crushed
- 1$^1/_2$lbs/ 700g / 3 cups fresh or frozen sweetcorn
- $^1/_2$ green pepper, chopped
- 1 tsp dried mixed herbs
- Salt and freshly ground black pepper

Method

1. Bring the stock to a boil and add the potatoes, onion and garlic and cook until potatoes are just tender.

2. Puree the soup and return to the pan. Add the sweetcorn, green pepper and dried mixed herbs, and cook for 5 minutes. Season and serve!

Courgette Noodles

Serves

Ingredients

- 1 courgette
- 1 tsp coconut oil
- 1 clove of garlic, chopped finely
- 2 tsp basil pesto
- 1 tbsp fromage frais
- 2 tbsp of fresh or frozen peas
- Salt and pepper
- Lemon zest to finish

This can also be made in week 1 of the detox if you exclude the coconut oil & fromage frais!
If you make this when you are not on a detox, you may add grated Parmesan cheese, if liked!

Method

1 Grate the courgette in long strokes along the grater.

2 Gently fry the courgette with the garlic. Stir in the pesto, fromage frais and the frozen peas.

3 Stir until coated, season with salt and pepper, then take off the heat.

4 Serve on a bed of green leaves!

Egg Fried Rice

Ingredients

Serves

- 4fl oz / 125ml brown basmati rice
- 1 large egg, beaten
- 2 spring onions
- Pinch of salt
- 1 tbsp oil

Method

1 Cook the rice for 15 minutes in a pan with a lid, on a low heat, without stirring or lifting the lid.

2 Allow the rice to go cold and fluff it up with a fork.

3 Fry the onions with half the oil for 3 minutes. Add lemon juice and pepper.

4 Next add the rest of the oil to the pan with the rice and cook for 30 seconds.

5 Continue to spread the ingredients around the pan and add the beaten egg.

6 Finally, add the spring onion and soy sauce. To bulk this out I love adding shiitake mushrooms or green vegetables, with tuna fish!

Garlic Prawns with Spaghetti

Serves  1 2

Ingredients

- 3¹/₂oz / 100g / ¹/₂ cup wholemeal spaghetti
- 2 tsps coconut oil
- 1 clove garlic, crushed
- 7oz / 200g / 1 cup cooked and peeled prawns
- 1 tsp lemon juice
- A handful fresh basil, chopped
- Salt and freshly ground black pepper

Method

1 Cook the pasta in plenty of salted water until al dente. Drain and reserve a little of the cooking liquid.

2 While the pasta is cooking, melt the coconut oil in a pan. Add the garlic and prawns, and cook for about 3 minutes, stirring occasionally.

3 Add the cooked pasta with just a little bit of the cooking liquid, the lemon juice and the chopped basil. Toss together thoroughly, season, and serve!

Halibut & Fennel Salad

Serves

 1 2 3 4

Ingredients

- 1 tsp ground coriander
- 1/2 tsp ground cumin
- 1 tbsp extra virgin olive oil
- 2 garlic cloves
- 4 x 6oz / 170g halibut fillets
- 1 tsp coconut oil

Ingredients
for the Salad

- 1 small fennel bulb, chopped
- 1/2 a red onion, chopped
- 2 tbsp fresh lemon juice
- 1 bunch chopped flat leaf parsley
- 1 handful thyme leaves

Did you know?

The anethole in fennel has repeatedly been shown to reduce inflammation and also helps prevent the occurrence of cancer

Method

1. Combine coriander, cumin and oil with garlic cloves, and rub on fish.

2. Heat 1 tsp coconut oil in a pan and add fish.

3. Cook for around 5 minutes on each side.

4. Combine salad ingredients and serve with fish!

HOT
Smoked Mackerel & Vegetable Medley

Serves

1 2

Ingredients

- 1 pack / 210g hot smoked mackerel fillets (or other flavour, but check the label for nasties!)
- 1 can (15oz/ 400g) chopped tomatoes
- 1/2 tsp medium curry powder (optional)
- 8oz / 225g / 1 cup frozen mixed vegetables
- Salt and freshly ground black pepper

Method

1 Put the chopped tomatoes in a pan with the curry powder (if using) and vegetables and cook.

2 Heat the fish according to the instructions.

3 Season the vegetables and tomatoes, and serve with the fish!

Kelp Pot Noodle

Ingredients

Serves 1

- 1¼oz / 35g raw kelp noodles
- Pinch of dried dulse or other seaweed/sea vegetable
- ½ tsp of grated fresh ginger (unpeeled if organic)
- 1 tbsp chopped fresh coriander or mint
- 2 tsps vegetable bouillon powder
- ½ tsp Chinese 5 spice
- A squeeze of lemon or lime juice

Plus: your choice of steamed veg, such as green beans, broccoli and cabbage, and raw veg, such as sliced mushrooms, peppers, pak choi, spring onions, grated carrot and courgette

Optional: a few tablespoons of cooked quinoa

Method

1. Rinse the kelp noodles and drain.

2. Add everything to a heatproof jar, with the miso. Keep refrigerated until ready to eat.

3. When you want to eat the pot noodle, add boiled water from a kettle and leave for 5–7 minutes. Give it a stir and eat. You can add soy sauce if you want!

VEGETARIAN ONLY

Lentil & Red Pepper SOUP

Serves

Ingredients

- 1 carton (400g) Free & Easy Organic Lentil & Red Pepper Soup

Have a different soup if you prefer, but check the label carefully as it many contain sugar and/or dairy, amongst other things!

Method

1 Heat and enjoy!

VEGETARIAN ONLY

Lentil & Vegetable
CURRY

Serves  1 2

Ingredients

- 1 can green lentils, drained and rinsed
- 8oz / 225g / 1 cup frozen mixed vegetables
- 1tbsp curry powder
- Fistful of sultanas
- 1 bag (250g) ready cooked brown basmati rice

Method

1 Boil the mixed vegetables. Drain off all but a small amount of the cooking liquid, add the lentils, curry powder, and sultanas, and heat through.

2 Heat the rice according to the instructions. Serve the curry on a bed of rice.

VEGETARIAN ONLY

b·r

Lentil & Vegetable SOUP

Serves 1 2 3 4

Ingredients

- 8oz / 225g / 1 cup red lentils
- 2 pints / 1135mls vegetable stock or water
- 1 large onion
- 2 large carrots, grated
- 2 large potatoes, peeled and diced
- Salt and black pepper to season

Plus any of the following:

- 2 sticks celery, chopped
- 1 courgette, sliced
- Handful chopped green beans
- 1/4 cabbage, shredded
- 1 parsnip, diced
- 2 cloves garlic, crushed or finely chopped
- Curry or chilli powder to your taste

For detox week 1, replace potatoes with sweet potatoes! At any other time you can either use potatoes, replace with sweet potatoes, or use one of each!

Method

1 Put the stock or water with the lentils in a large pan. Bring to the boil and cook vigorously for around ten minutes.

2 Add the rest of the ingredients and simmer for around 20 minutes, or until vegetable are tender. Season with salt and pepper then serve!

Mediterranean Roasted Vegetables

Serves  ① ②

 Ingredients

This can also be made in week 1 of the detox if you exclude the olive oil!

- 1 tray pre-prepared vegetables (Most supermarkets sell this in an oven-ready tray, so you save on washing up, too!)
- 1tbsp olive oil
- Salt and freshly ground black pepper

 Method

1 Add the olive oil to the tray of veg and mix thoroughly, then season.

2 Bake in the oven according to the instructions and serve immediately!

Minestrone Soup

Serves 1 2 3 4

Ingredients

- 1 tbsp olive oil
- 1 onion, chopped
- 3 garlic cloves, thinly sliced
- 1 leek, washed and sliced
- 1 large carrot, peeled and diced
- 2 celery stalks, trimmed and chopped
- 1 potato, peeled and diced

- 1 tbsp tomato purée
- 15oz / 400g tin chopped tomatoes
- 1 bouquet garni
- 2 pints / 1135mls vegetable stock
- 4oz / 115g / 1/4 cup peas (fresh or frozen)
- 4oz / 115g / 1 cup wholemeal pasta
- 1 handful fresh flat leaf parsley, finely chopped

make this recipe Gluten-Free by using gluten-free pasta!

see Method overleaf!

Minestrone Soup
CONTINUED

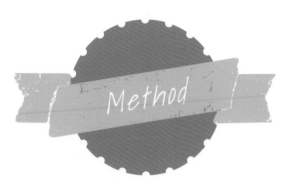

Method

1 Heat the oil in a large saucepan over a medium heat. Add the onion, garlic and leek and sauté for 4-5 minutes.

2 Add the carrots, celery, and potato and cook for a further 4-5 minutes, stirring occasionally.

3 Stir in the tomato purée and cook for 1 minute, then add the tomatoes, bouquet garni and stock and bring to the boil. Reduce the heat, then simmer gently for 15 minutes.

4 Add the peas and pasta and bring back to the boil. Reduce the heat and simmer for 8-10 minutes, until the pasta is tender. Discard the bouquet garni.

5 Serve garnished with parsley, and Parmesan if liked!

Nut Bread

Ingredients

Serves

- 9oz / 250g almonds
- 9oz / 250g quinoa flakes or brown rice
- 10 1/2oz / 300g pumpkin seeds
- 7oz / 200g sunflower seeds
- 2 tbsp chia seeds
- 3 heaped tbsp psyllium husk powder
- 2 tbsp dried mixed herbs

Helpful Tip!

Storing the bread in the fridge makes it last longer, and you can freeze it, too!

Method

1 Place the almonds, quinoa flakes and half the pumpkin seeds in a food processor and process until smooth.

2 Place the mix in a bowl with the remaining pumpkin seeds and the sunflower seeds, chia seeds, psyllium husk, dried herbs and salt to taste.

3 Add 3 cups of cold water and let the mixture sit for an hour.

4 Heat the oven to 180°C / 350°F / gas mark 4.

5 Once the mixture is really firm, grease the base of a loaf tin with coconut or olive oil, pour the mixture in and press it down with a spoon. Bake in the oven for 40 minutes to an hour, until the top begins to brown and you can pull a knife out of the middle without any of the mixture sticking to it. Finally, slice, smother on your favourite toppings and enjoy!

Pasta & Tomato Sauce
WITH SALAD

Serves

Ingredients

- 3oz / 85g / 3/4 cup wholemeal pasta
- 1 can (15oz / 400g) chopped tomatoes
- 8-10 black olives, sliced
- 4-6 sundried tomatoes, not in oil and chopped
- 1tbsp capers
- 1 tsp basil
- 1 tsp oregano
- Salt and freshly ground black pepper

Ingredients
for the Salad

- Little Gem lettuce
- Cherry tomatoes
- Cucumber
- Peppers

Method

1 Put the pasta on to cook.

2 Add all other ingredients to a pan, stir, and heat thoroughly.

3 When the pasta is cooked, drain it thoroughly, add to the sauce and mix to combine.

4 Serve with a fresh, crisp salad made from the ingredients listed, or those of your own choice. (Add dressing as desired.)

Quinoa Salad

Serves

Ingredients

- 9oz / 250g / 1 cup cooked quinoa
- 2 celery sticks
- 2 spring onions
- 1lb / 500g / 2 cups grapes
- 1 lime, juiced
- 2 tbsp olive oil
- 1 handful mint
- 1 handful basil
- Pinch of salt

Method

1 Place all ingredients in a bowl and mix together for a very tasty and filling salad!

Quinoa Salad WITH Avocado & Strawberries

Serves

Ingredients

- 4oz / 115g / 1/2 cup cooked quinoa
- 1 bag baby rocket leaves
- 1 tbsp chopped fresh mint
- 2 tbsp chopped fresh coriander
- 4 spring onions, chopped
- 1/2 avocado, sliced
- 6-8 strawberries, sliced
- 1 tbsp olive oil
- 1 tbsp lemon juice
- Salt and freshly ground black pepper

Method

1 Combine the quinoa with the leaves, vegetables and fruit in a bowl

2 Whip the oil and lemon juice together; add to the bowl and mix thoroughly. Season and serve!

Root Vegetable SOUP

Serves 1 2

Ingredients

- 3 carrots
- 1 parsnip
- 1 turnip
- 1 leek, sliced
- 1/2 onion, chopped
- Salt and pepper to taste
- 9fl oz / 250mls water / vegetable stock

A gorgeously filling soup that is quick and easy to make!

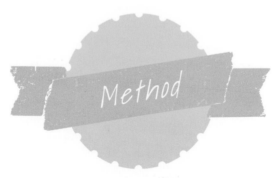

Method

1 Bake the vegetables in the oven on 200°C / 390°F / gas mark 6 for about 30 minutes.

2 Add to the vegetables to a blender with the hot water and stock; process until smooth.

3 Serve piping hot!

Salmon Steaks & Green Salad

Serves

Ingredients

- 4 salmon steaks
- Juice of a lemon
- Salt and freshly ground black pepper
- 2 little gem lettuce, washed, dried and
- chopped.
- 1/2 cucumber, finely sliced
- 2 stalks celery, finely sliced
- 1 bulb fennel, finely sliced

Method

1 Place the salmon steaks in a baking dish lined with parchment paper, sprinkle with lemon juice and season with salt and pepper.

2 Bake, uncovered, at 200°C / 390°F / gas mark 6 for 15-20 minutes or until the fish flakes easily with a fork.

3 Meanwhile, prepare the salad, combine all ingredients and dress with lemon juice.

4 Serve the salmon steaks with the green salad and enjoy!

Scallops WITH Green Beans & Broccoli

Serves

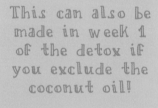

Ingredients

- 6oz / 170g / ½ cup green beans
- 1 large head broccoli, broken into florets
- 1 tbsp coconut oil
- 6-8 scallops
- 1 clove garlic, chopped
- Juice of half a lime
- Salt and freshly ground black pepper

This can also be made in week 1 of the detox if you exclude the coconut oil!

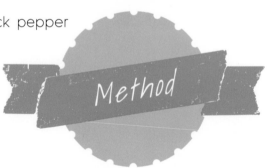

Method

1 Put the vegetables on to steam for 5 minutes.

2 Heat the coconut oil in a frying pan and add the garlic and the scallops. Fry the scallops for 1-2 minutes, until golden, then turn them over cook for 1-2 minutes more.

3 Transfer to plates with the vegetables. Squeeze the lime over the scallops, season with salt and pepper, and serve immediately!

Sea Bream & Vegetables

Ingredients

Serves

- 4 x 160g / 5½oz sea bream fillets
- 6 cloves of garlic
- 1 small dried chilli
- Rosemary
- Himalayan salt
- ½ lemon
- 4 heads broccoli
- 12oz / 340g / 1½ cups green beans

Method

1. Preheat oven to 200°C / 390°F / gas mark 6.

2. Put the garlic cloves (skin left on) in a tin and roast in the oven for 15 minutes.

3. When the garlic is cooked, place the fillets on some parchment paper and squeeze over the roasted garlic.

4. Scatter the dried chilli and rosemary leaves, and season with salt and pepper.

5. Seal the parchment paper around the fish and roast in the oven for 8–10 minutes. While the fish is roasting, steam the broccoli and green beans for 5–10 minutes.

6. Serve with steamed broccoli and green beans!

Smoked Salmon & Salad

Serves

1 2 3 4

Ingredients

- 7oz / 200g / scant 1 cup smoked salmon
- 1 lemon
- 2 small avocados
- 1/2 cucumber
- Selection of fresh herbs
- 1 tbsp of roasted seeds

Method

1 Place the salmon in a bowl and squeeze the juice of the lemon on it.

2 Slice the avocado and cucumber and place in the bowl with the salmon.

3 Add the fresh herbs and seeds

Speedy Stir-Fry

Serves

1 2 3 4

Ingredients

- 1 tbsp coconut oil
- 1 bag prepared stir-fry vegetables
- Fistful cashew nuts
- 1tsp Chinese 5-spice
- 1 bag (250g) ready cooked brown rice

Method

1 Heat the rice according to the instructions and keep warm

2 Heat the coconut oil in a wok and add the vegetables and 5-spice; stir fry until cooked.

3 Add the rice and toss together, then serve!

Spicy Parsnip Soup

Ingredients

Serves

- 1 tbsp coconut oil
- 1 large onion, chopped
- 2 cloves garlic, crushed
- 2lbs / 1kg / 4 cups parsnips, peeled and chopped roughly
- 2 tsps ground coriander seeds
- 1 tsp ground turmeric
- 1 tsp medium curry powder
- 1 tsp ground ginger
- 2 pints / 1.2L water
- Salt and freshly ground black pepper

This can also be made in week 1 of the detox if you exclude the coconut oil!

Method

1 Melt the coconut oil in a large saucepan stir-fry the onion for 5 minutes, adding the garlic and spices for the last minute.

2 Add the parsnips, stir to cover with the oils and spices, then add the water. Bring to the boil and simmer for about 25 minutes, stirring occasionally, until the parsnips are soft.

3 Allow to cool slightly, then blend in a liquidiser. Season with salt and freshly ground black pepper, reheat as necessary, and serve!

Smoked Salmon
& shop-bought Salad

Serves

Ingredients

This can also be made in week 1 of the detox if you exclude the olive oil!

- 4oz / 115g / 1/2 cup smoked salmon
- 1 tray of salad from supermarket salad bar
- 1 tsp olive oil
- Salt and freshly ground black pepper

Method

1 Pile everything onto a plate, dress with the oil, season with salt and pepper and enjoy!

Spicy Tomato & Veg SOUP

Serves 1 2

Ingredients

- 1 can (15oz / 400g) chopped tomatoes
- 1/2 pint / 285mls water
- 1/2 tsp chilli powder (or to taste)
- 1 clove garlic, crushed
- 1 large carrot, sliced
- 1 head broccoli, broken into florets
- 1 small cauliflower, broken into florets

Method

1 Put all the ingredients into a saucepan, bring to the boil then simmer until the vegetables are tender!

2 Blend together until smooth and enjoy!

Spicy Vegetable Stew

Ingredients

Serves

- 1 large onion, thinly sliced
- 3 garlic cloves, crushed
- 1/2 pint / 285mls vegetable stock
- 1 tbsp chilli powder (or to taste)
- 1 tsp ground coriander
- 1 large sweet potato, peeled and chopped
- 2 cans chopped tomatoes
- 2 courgettes, finely diced
- 7oz / 200g / 1 cup bag baby spinach
- 4 tbsp chopped coriander

Method

1 Dry fry the onion and garlic in a non-stick pan for 3-4 minutes, then pour in the stock and add the chilli powder, coriander and sweet potato. Bring to the boil and simmer for ten minutes.

2 Add the tomatoes and courgettes; bring back to the boil and simmer for another 10 minutes.

3 Using a slotted spoon, fish out about half the sweet potato and mash it, then return to the post and stir through (to thicken it slightly).

4 Fold in the spinach so that it wilts into the pan.

5 Serve in bowls, garnished with the chopped coriander and enjoy!

Sweet Potato with Roasted Vegetables

Ingredients

Serves

- 4 sweet potatoes
- 1 swede
- 2 carrots
- 2 parsnips
- 2 onions
- 3 whole garlic bulbs
- Rosemary leaves
- Salt and pepper

Method

1 Preheat your oven to 200°C (fan 180°C) / 390°F/ gas mark 6

2 Peel the vegetables, and halve and slice lengthways. Leave the garlic bulbs whole. Pick the rosemary leaves.

3 Boil the sweet potatoes, swede and carrots for 5 minutes, then add the parsnips and cook for a further 4 minutes. Drain the vegetables.

4 Put the parboiled vegetables into a roasting tray with salt and pepper. Spread them out evenly in one layer. Put them into the preheated oven for about 45 minutes. Add the onion, rosemary and garlic and cook for 20 minutes more. Serve with a vegetable stock gravy!

Thai Prawn Soup

Ingredients

Serves

- 8 spring onions, finely shredded
- 2 fresh lemongrass stalks, very finely shredded
- 1 garlic clove, peeled and crushed
- 1 inch finely grated fresh root ginger
- 1/2 red chilli, deseeded and finely sliced
- 900ml / 1$\frac{1}{2}$ pints of vegetable stock
- 2oz / 60g / 1/2 cup shiitake mushrooms
- 2oz / 60g / 1/2 cup mange tout
- 7oz / 200g / 1 cup raw tiger prawns, peeled and deveined
- Pinch of himalayan salt
- Handful of chopped coriander leaves

Method

1 Place the spring onions, lemongrass, garlic, ginger, chilli and stock in a large saucepan, cover and bring to the boil.

2 Add the mushrooms and mangetout to the pan. Cook for 3 minutes then add the prawns and himalayan salt. Cook for a further 2-3 minutes until the prawns turn pink. Take off the heat.

3 Stir in the coriander and serve straight away!

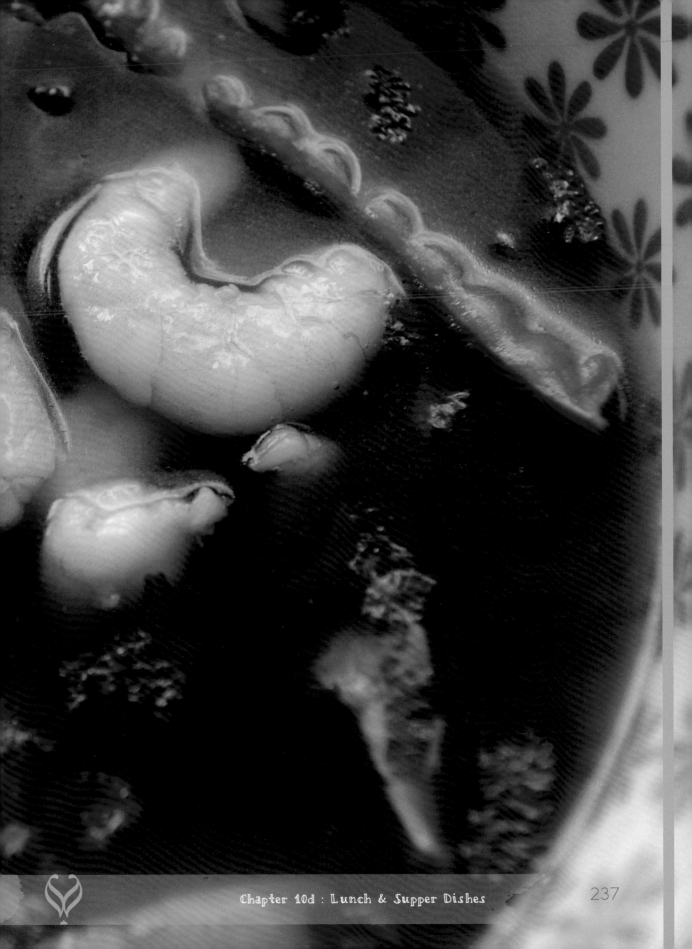

Thai Vegetable Soup

Serves

1 2 3 4

Ingredients

- 2 pints / 1 litre vegetable stock
- Thumb sized piece of ginger, cut into matchsticks
- 2 cloves garlic, cut into matchsticks
- 1 stalk lemon grass, chopped
- 1 head pak choi, shredded
- 1 carrot, julienned
- 4 spring onions, chopped
- 2 radishes, cut into matchsticks
- Pinch of himalayan salt

Method

1 Bring the stock to the boil, add the ginger, garlic and lemon grass and simmer for 2–3 minutes.

2 Add the rest of the prepared vegetables and simmer for 2–3 minutes.

3 Season with himalayan salt and serve!

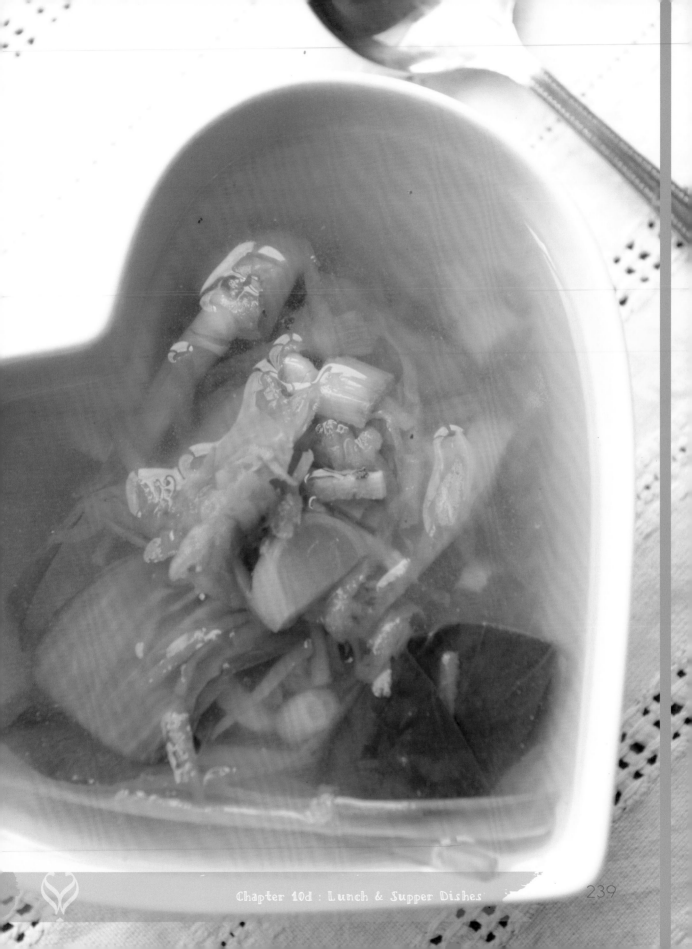

Tuna Salad

Serves  1

Ingredients

- 1 tray / shop bought salad
- 1 can tuna in spring water
- 1 lemon

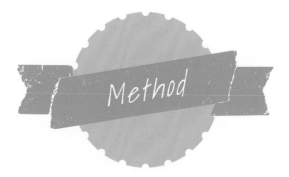

Method

1 Drain the tuna, add to the salad and dress with freshly squeezed lemon juice!

Vegetable Stew

Ingredients

Serves

- 1 tbsp olive oil
- 2 large onions, chopped
- 3 cloves garlic, crushed or finely chopped
- 2 tsps caraway seeds
- 2 large carrots, sliced
- 1 leek, chopped
- 3 large potatoes, diced

- 2 stalks celery, chopped
- 1 1/2 pints / 850mls vegetable stock or water
- 1 bay leaf
- 1/2 tsp dried thyme
- 1/2 tsp dried marjoram
- 4oz / 115g / 1/2 cup peas, fresh or frozen
- 1 tbsp ground chia seeds

Method

1. Heat the olive oil in a large pan; add the onions and sauté for a couple of minutes then add the garlic and the caraway seeds and sauté for another couple of minutes.

2. Add the remaining prepared vegetables (all but the peas) to the pan and mix until coated in oil.

3. Add the vegetable stock, dried herbs and bay leaf. Bring to the boil, then turn down the heat and simmer for 20 minutes, stirring occasionally.

4. After 20 minutes add the peas and cook for a further ten minutes until vegetables are tender and peas are cooked.

5. Add the chia seeds and stir, to thicken. Serve in bowls with crusty bread for dipping!

Watercress Soup

Serves

1 2 3 4

Ingredients

- 1 tsp olive oil
- 2 shallots, finely chopped
- 2 medium potatoes, peeled and diced
- 2 pints water
- 7oz / 200g / 1 cup watercress
- Salt and freshly ground black pepper

This soup can be served hot or cold - store in the fridge and / or add ice cubes for a chilled soup. If you wish, add a swirl of natural yogurt to garnish!

Method

1 Heat the olive oil in a pan and sauté the shallots until soft.

2 Add the potatoes and cook for a minute or two, then add the water. Bring to the boil and simmer for about 15 minutes, stirring occasionally, until the potatoes are soft..

3 Add the watercress and cook for a couple of minutes.

4 Allow to cool slightly, then blend in a liquidiser. Season with salt and freshly ground black pepper, reheat as necessary, and serve!

Avocado & Prawn Salad

This is a new twist on an old favourite!

Serves 1 2 3 4

Ingredients

- 6 tbsps fromage frais
- 1 tbsp tomato puree
- 2 tbsps fresh chives, chopped
- 8oz / 225g / 1 cup cooked prawns
- Salt and pepper
- 2 avocados, ripe and ready to eat
- Paprika
- Rocket
- Lemon wedges

Method

1. In a bowl, mix the fromage frais and tomato puree. Stir in the chopped chives and the prawns, and season with salt and pepper.

2. Halve each avocado lengthwise and remove the stone. Spoon the prawn mixture into the avocado halves, and dust with paprika.

3. Place each avocado half on a bed of rocket and serve garnished with lemon wedges.

Watch how to make this here!
http://www.thebodyrescueplan.com/prawn-and-avocado-salad/

RICE FREE

Vegetable Sushi

Serves 1

Ingredients

- 1 nori sheet
- 1 egg
- 1 tbsp mung bean sprouts
- 1/2 avocado

Did you know?

Nori seaweed is incredibly rich in nutrients - it is especially high in iron and omega 3; it also helps lower cholesterol too!

Method

1 Lay nori sheet on a sushi bamboo mat.

2 Cut the sheets in half and dampen with some water.

3 Make the omelette: whisk the egg, then add the mung beans. Cook in an omelette pan for 4–5 minutes.

4 Place the omelette and avocado on the nori sheet, and roll up.

5 Cut the roll into 2 inch sections and serve!

Shopping lists

CHAPTER 11

I have provided shopping lists for both weeks of each of the meal plans!

The lists include an amount of nuts, seeds and dried fruit to cover your daily allowance. If you prefer different ones to those listed, be sure to add or change them.

If a recipe used calls for more than a moderate amount of nuts, seeds or dried fruit (a handful, or one or two tablespoons) then the additional amount has been included in the list to make sure you have sufficient!

If you plan to substitute any of the snacks listed with fruit, vegetables, Nakd bars or nori strips, remember to make the appropriate adjustments to the shopping list too!

A little something to Save you Time!

Low on time and need to go shopping? Head over to the link below and enter this code;

TBRP3

to download your free shopping list for each of the meal plans!

www.thebodyrescueplan.com/shoppinglist/

Summer Week 1

Fresh Veg

4lbs / 2kg carrots
4 onions
2 red onions
2 bunches spring onions
1 parsnip
2 large leeks
4 bunches asparagus spears
7 heads broccoli
1 small cauliflower
1 turnip
3 sweet potatoes
4 large portobello mushrooms
2oz / 60g shiitake mushrooms
2oz / 60g mangetout
1 red chilli
3 courgettes
1 green pepper
1 red pepper
2 small avocados
2 large avocados
18oz / 500g green beans
3 cucumbers
1 bulb fennel
1 head pak choi
1 bunch of kale
1 bunch / bag of watercress
1 bag of spinach
7oz / 200g bag baby spinach
2 bags rocket

1 head romaine lettuce
2 heads of little gem lettuce
1 head of celery
1 bag or bunch of radishes
1 punnet cherry tomatoes
1 beef tomato
1 tray shop bought salad (or buy extra veg to prep your own)
5 bulbs of garlic

Fresh Fruit

9 apples
2 oranges (for juice)
1 punnet blueberries
1 punnet strawberries
6 lemons
1 lime
1 mango
1 pineapple
1 small bunch grapes
10 dates
4 1/2 oz / 130g Medjool dates

Dried Fruit

Raisins (8oz / 225g for recipes)
Apricots (4oz / 115g for recipes)
Sultanas
Dates (4oz / 115g for recipes)
Figs (12oz / 250g for recipes)

The Body Rescue Detox Recipe Book

Fish & Shellfish

4 salmon steaks
7oz / 200g smoked salmon
4 x 160g / 5½oz sea bream fillets
7oz / 200g raw tiger prawns
1 pack (210g) hot smoked mackerel fillets
1 can tuna in spring water

Nuts & Seeds

Flaxseeds
Chia seeds
Sunflower seeds
Pumpkin seeds
Almonds (6oz / 185g for recipes)
Cashews (4oz / 115g for recipes)
Walnuts
Hazelnuts
Brazil nuts
1 bag ground almonds

Herbs & Spices

Dried

Oregano
Ground coriander
Dried mixed herbs
Vanilla seeds
Cinnamon
Nutmeg
Ground cumin
Smoked paprika

Chilli powder
Curry powder
Cayenne pepper
Garlic powder

Fresh

Parsley
Basil
Rosemary
Coriander
Mint
Root ginger
3 stalks lemongrass

Other

17 eggs
1 Nakd bar
Maca powder
Nori strips
1¼ oz / 35g raw kelp noodles
Dulse or other seaweed/sea vegetable
1 bottle dark soy sauce (sugar free)
Tamari
Vanilla extract
4 cans / cartons (15oz / 400g) chopped tomatoes
8oz / 225g frozen mixed vegetables
Vegetable stock / stock cubes / powder
Himalayan salt
Black pepper

Summer Week 2

Fresh Veg

7 carrots

3 onions

1 red onion

2 bunches spring onions

4 shallots

6oz / 175g peas (fresh or frozen)

1 1/2 lbs / 700g sweetcorn kernels (fresh or frozen)

1 1/2 lbs / 750g parsnips

1 small red beetroot

1 leek

1 bunch asparagus spears

2 heads broccoli

2 medium cauliflowers

1 medium white cabbage

1 medium red cabbage

4lbs / 2kg potatoes

4 sweet potatoes

4 chestnut mushrooms

6 mushrooms

6 button mushrooms

2 large courgettes

1 green pepper

1 yellow pepper

1 tray pre-prepared Mediterranean vegetables (or buy extra veg to prep your own)

3oz / 85g bean sprouts

1 avocado

6oz / 170g green beans

2 cucumbers

1 bunch of kale

2 bags spinach

2 x 7oz / 200g bag of watercress

1 bag baby rocket leaves

2 heads of little gem lettuce

2 heads of celery

1 punnet cherry tomatoes

1 bulb fennel

2 bulbs of garlic

Fresh Fruit

7 apples

1 banana

1 pound plantains or green bananas

1 pear

2 kiwi fruit

1 punnet strawberries

1 punnet raspberries

1 punnet blackberries

4 lemons

1 lime

4oz / 115g red seedless grapes

4oz / 115g green seedless grapes

1 pot prepared chopped fruit (or buy extra fruit to prep your own)

Dried Fruit

Raisins (8oz / 225g for recipes)
Apricots (4oz / 115g for recipes)
Sultanas
Dates (4oz / 115g for recipes)
Figs

Fish & Shellfish

4oz / 115g smoked salmon
6-8 scallops
2 cod steaks, approx. 1 inch thick, 6oz / 170g
4 salmon steaks

Nuts & Seeds

Flaxseeds
Chia seeds
Sunflower seeds (7oz / 200g for recipes)
Pumpkin seeds (10 1/2 oz / 300g for recipes)
Almonds (13oz / 365g for recipes)
Cashews (4oz / 115g for recipes)
Walnuts
Hazelnuts
Brazil nuts

Herbs & Spices

Dried

Bay leaves
Thyme
Marjoram
Oregano
Caraway seeds
Basil
Tarragon
Sage
Dried mixed herbs
Cinnamon

Ground ginger
Nutmeg
Ground mixed spice
Garlic powder

Fresh

Parsley
Coriander
Mint
Root ginger

Other

1lb / 450g quinoa
9oz / 250g quinoa flakes or brown rice
3oz / 85g wholemeal pasta
2 1/2 oz / 75g porridge oats
6 eggs
2 large (500g) pots natural yogurt
1 small pot natural yogurt
1 small pot fromage frais
Greek yogurt
Almond nut butter
1 Nakd bar
Maca powder
Psyllium husk powder
Nori strips
Vanilla extract
2 cans / cartons (15oz / 400g) chopped tomatoes
Wasabi paste
Light soy sauce
1 jar basil pesto
1 jar capers
1 jar / packet black olives
1 jar / packet sundried tomatoes
Vegetable stock / stock cubes / powder
Himalayan salt
Black pepper
Extra virgin olive oil
Coconut oil

Winter Week 1

Fresh Veg

5lbs / 2¹/₂kg carrots
6 onions
2 red onions
2 bunches spring onions
4 parsnips
3 leeks
4 bunches asparagus spears
7 heads broccoli
1 small cauliflower
1 bag of spinach
2 turnips
1 swede
6 sweet potatoes
8 large portobello mushrooms
2oz / 60g shiitake mushrooms
2oz / 60g mangetout
1 red chilli
1 green pepper
2 large avocados
18oz / 500g green beans
3 cucumbers
1 bulb fennel
1 head pak choi
1 bunch of kale
1 bunch / bag of watercress
2 bags rocket
1 head romaine lettuce
2 heads of little gem lettuce

2 heads of celery
1 bag or bunch of radishes
1 punnet cherry tomatoes
1 beef tomato
1 tray shop bought salad (or buy extra veg to prep your own)
5 bulbs of garlic

Fresh Fruit

11 apples
2 oranges (for juice)
1 punnet blueberries
6 lemons
1 lime
1 mango
1 pineapple
1 small bunch grapes
10 dates
4¹/₂oz / 130g Medjool dates

Dried Fruit

Raisins (8oz / 225g for recipes)
Apricots (4oz / 115g for recipes)
Sultanas
Dates (4oz / 115g for recipes)
Figs (12oz / 250g for recipes)

Fish & Shellfish

4 salmon steaks

4 x 160g /5½oz sea bream fillets
7oz / 200g raw tiger prawns
1 pack (210g) hot smoked mackerel
fillets
1 can tuna in spring water

Rosemary
Coriander
Mint
Root ginger
3 stalks lemongrass

Nuts & Seeds

Flaxseeds
Chia seeds
Sunflower seeds
Pumpkin seeds
Almonds (6oz / 185g for recipes)
Cashews (4oz / 115g for recipes)
Walnuts
Hazelnuts
Brazil nuts

Herbs & Spices

Dried
Oregano
Dried mixed herbs
Vanilla seeds
Cinnamon
Nutmeg
Ground cumin
Smoked paprika
Chilli powder
1 small dried chilli
Chinese 5 spice
Curry powder
Cayenne pepper
Garlic powder

Fresh
Parsley

Other

21 eggs
Maca powder
Nori strips
1¼oz / 35g raw kelp noodles
Dulse or other seaweed / sea vegetable
1 bottle dark soy sauce (sugar free)
Tamari
Vanilla extract
2 cans / cartons (15oz / 400g)
chopped tomatoes
8oz / 225g frozen mixed vegetables
Vegetable stock / stock cubes / powder
Himalayan salt
Black pepper

Winter Week 2

Fresh Veg

5 carrots

6 onions

1 bunch spring onions

3 shallots

10oz / 280g peas (fresh or frozen)

1¹⁄₂ lbs / 700g sweetcorn kernels
(fresh or frozen)

6oz / 170g baby sweetcorn

3¹⁄₄ lbs / 1.6kg parsnips

1 small red beetroot

2 leeks

2 heads broccoli

2 medium cauliflowers

1 medium white cabbage

1 medium red cabbage

3lbs / 1.5kg potatoes

10 sweet potatoes

1 celeriac

10oz / 280g chestnut mushrooms

6 mushrooms

6 button mushrooms

2 courgettes

1 green pepper

2 red peppers

1 yellow pepper

1 tray pre-prepared Mediterranean
vegetables (or buy extra veg to prep
your own)

3oz / 85g bean sprouts

1 avocado

6oz / 170g green beans

1 cucumber

1 bunch of kale

1 bag spinach

7oz / 200g bag baby spinach

2 heads of celery

1 punnet cherry tomatoes

1 large tomato

3 bulbs of garlic

1 bag prepared stir-fry vegetables (or
buy extra veg to prep your own)

Fresh Fruit

3 apples

1 banana

1 pound plantains or green bananas

3 lemons

2 limes

20 dates

Dried Fruit

Raisins (8oz / 225g for recipes)

Apricots (4oz / 115g for recipes)

Sultanas

Dates (4oz / 115g for recipes)

Figs

Fish & Shellfish

4oz / 115g smoked salmon
6-8 scallops
7oz / 200g cooked and peeled prawns

Nuts & Seeds

Flaxseeds
Chia seeds
Sunflower seeds (7oz / 200g for recipes)
Pumpkin seeds (10½ oz / 300g for recipes)
Almonds (13oz / 365g for recipes)
Cashews (4oz / 115g for recipes)
Walnuts
Hazelnuts
Brazil nuts
1 bag ground almonds

Herbs & Spices

Dried
Bay leaves
Thyme
Marjoram
Caraway seeds
Oregano
Basil
Tarragon
Sage
Ground coriander seeds
Bouquet garni
Dried mixed herbs
Cinnamon
Ground ginger
Nutmeg
Ground mixed spice
Paprika
Ground turmeric

Chinese 5 spice
Medium curry powder
Chilli
Garlic powder

Fresh
Coriander
Mint
Basil
Root ginger

Other

12oz / 340g quinoa
9oz / 250g quinoa flakes or brown rice
3½ oz / 100g wholemeal spaghetti
7oz / 200g wholemeal pasta
1 bag ready cooked brown rice
4fl oz / 125ml brown basmati rice
4 eggs
2 large (500g) pots natural yogurt
1 small pot fromage frais
Maca powder
Psyllium husk powder
Nori strips
Vanilla extract
4 cans / cartons (15oz / 400g) chopped tomatoes
Wasabi paste
Light soy sauce
Tomato puree
1 jar basil pesto
1 jar capers
1 jar / packet black olives
1 jar / packet sundried tomatoes
Vegetable stock / stock cubes / powder
Himalayan salt
Black pepper
Extra virgin olive oil
Coconut oil

Vegetarian Week 1

Fresh Veg

4lbs / 2kg carrots

10 onions

2 red onions

1 bunch spring onions

7 parsnips

3 large leeks

3 bunches asparagus spears

3 heads broccoli

1 small cauliflower

1 cabbage

2 turnips

2 swedes

13 sweet potatoes

8 large portobello mushrooms

3 courgettes

1 green pepper

1 red pepper

2 large avocados

10oz / 275g green beans

3 cucumbers

1 head pak choi

1 bunch of kale

1 bunch / bag of watercress

1 bag of spinach

7oz / 200g bag baby spinach

2 bags rocket

1 head romaine lettuce

2 heads of little gem lettuce

2 heads of celery

1 bag or bunch of radishes

1 punnet cherry tomatoes

1lb / 450g salad tomatoes

1 beef tomato

7 bulbs of garlic

Fresh Fruit

10 apples

2 oranges (for juice)

1 punnet blueberries

1 punnet strawberries

3 lemons

1 lime

1 mango

1 pineapple

1 small bunch grapes

10 dates

4oz / 115g dates

4 1/2 oz / 130g Medjool dates

Dried Fruit

Raisins (8oz / 225g for recipes)

Apricots (4oz / 115g for recipes)

Sultanas

Dates (4oz / 115g for recipes)

Figs (12 oz / 250g for recipes)

Nuts & Seeds

Flaxseeds

Chia seeds
Sunflower seeds
Pumpkin seeds
Almonds (2$\frac{1}{4}$oz / 68g for recipes)
Cashews (4oz / 115g for recipes)
Walnuts
Hazelnuts
Brazil nuts
1 bag ground almonds

Herbs & Spices

Dried

Oregano
Dried mixed herbs
Vanilla seeds
Cinnamon
Nutmeg
Ground cumin
Smoked paprika
Chilli powder
Curry powder
Cayenne pepper
Garlic powder
Chinese 5 spice

Fresh

Parsley
Rosemary
Coriander
Mint
Root ginger
1 stalk lemongrass

Other

21 eggs
Maca powder
Nori strips
1$\frac{1}{4}$oz / 35g raw kelp noodles
Dulse or other seaweed/sea vegetable
Tamari
Vanilla extract
8oz / 225g red lentils
3 cans / cartons (15oz / 400g) chopped tomatoes
1 can (400g) Free & Easy Organic Lentil & Red Pepper Soup
Vegetable stock / stock cubes / powder
Himalayan salt
Black pepper

Vegetarian Week 2

Fresh Veg

3lbs / 1.5kg carrots
4 onions
2 bunches spring onions
5 shallots
10oz / 280g peas (fresh or frozen)
1½lbs / 700g sweetcorn kernels (fresh or frozen)
6oz / 170g baby sweetcorn
3¼ lbs / 1.5kg parsnips
1 small red beetroot
4 leeks
1 head broccoli
2 medium cauliflowers
1 medium white cabbage
1 medium red cabbage
1 celeriac
4lbs / 2kg potatoes
4 sweet potatoes
8oz / 225g chestnut mushrooms
6 button mushrooms
1 green pepper
2 red pepper
1 tray pre-prepared Mediterranean vegetables (or buy extra veg to prep your own)
3oz / 85g bean sprouts
1 avocado
1 cucumber
1 bunch of kale

1 bag spinach
7oz / 200g bag of watercress
1 bag baby rocket leaves
2 heads of celery
1 punnet cherry tomatoes
1 large tomato
2 bulbs of garlic

Fresh Fruit

5 apples
1 banana
1 pound plantains or green bananas
1 punnet strawberries
1 punnet raspberries
1 punnet blackberries
3 lemons

Dried Fruit

Raisins (8oz / 225g for recipes)
Apricots (4oz / 115g for recipes)
Sultanas
Dates (4oz / 115g for recipes)
Figs

Nuts & Seeds

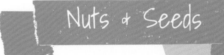

Flaxseeds
Chia seeds
Sunflower seeds (7oz / 200g for recipes)

Pumpkin seeds (10½oz / 300g for recipes)
Almonds (13oz / 365g for recipes)
Cashews (4oz / 115g for recipes)
Walnuts
Hazelnuts
Brazil nuts

Herbs & Spices

Dried

Bay leaves
Thyme
Marjoram
Oregano
Caraway seeds
Basil
Ground coriander seeds
Tarragon
Sage
Bouquet garni
Dried mixed herbs
Cinnamon
Ground ginger
Ground mixed spice
Paprika
Chilli
Curry powder
Turmeric
Garlic powder

Fresh

Coriander
Mint
Root ginger

Other

12oz / 340g quinoa
9oz / 250g quinoa flakes or brown rice
7oz / 200g wholemeal pasta
2½oz / 75g porridge oats
4fl oz / 125ml brown basmati rice
3 eggs
2 large (500g) pots natural yogurt
1 small pot natural yogurt
1 small pot fromage frais
1 Nakd bar
Maca powder
Psyllium husk powder
Nori strips
2 cans / cartons (15oz / 400g) chopped tomatoes
Wasabi paste
Light soy sauce
Tomato puree
1 jar basil pesto
1 jar capers
1 jar / packet black olives
1 jar / packet sundried tomatoes
Vegetable stock / stock cubes / powder
Himalayan salt
Black pepper
Extra virgin olive oil
Coconut oil

Fast Food Week 1

Fresh Veg

4lbs / 2kg carrots
6 onions
1 red onion
1 bunch spring onions
2 parsnips
3 leeks
4 bunches asparagus spears
8 heads broccoli
1 small cauliflower
2 turnips
1 sweet potato
4 large portobello mushrooms
2 courgettes
1 green pepper
2 small avocados
2 large avocados
18oz / 500g green beans
3 cucumbers
1 bulb fennel
1 head pak choi
1 bunch of kale
1 bunch / bag of watercress
1 bag of spinach
7oz / 200g bag baby spinach
2 bags rocket
1 head romaine lettuce
2 heads of little gem lettuce
1 head of celery
1 bag or bunch of radishes

1 punnet cherry tomatoes
1 beef tomato
2 trays shop bought salad
2 bulbs of garlic

Fresh Fruit

9 apples
2 oranges (for juice)
1 punnet blueberries
1 punnet strawberries
6 lemons
1 lime
1 mango
1 pineapple
1 small bunch grapes
4$\frac{1}{2}$oz / 130g Medjool dates

Dried Fruit

Raisins (8oz / 225g for recipes)
Apricots (4oz / 115g for recipes)
Sultanas
Dates (4oz / 115g for recipes)
Figs (12oz / 250g for recipes)

Fish & Shellfish

4 salmon steaks
7oz / 200g smoked salmon
4 x 160g / 5$\frac{1}{2}$oz sea bream fillets
1 pack (210g) hot smoked mackerel

fillets
2 cans tuna in spring water

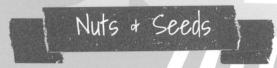
Nuts & Seeds

Flaxseeds
Chia seeds
Sunflower seeds
Pumpkin seeds
Almonds (6oz / 185g for recipes)
Cashews (4oz / 115g for recipes)
Walnuts
Hazelnuts
Brazil nuts

Herbs & Spices

Dried
Oregano
Ground coriander
Dried mixed herbs
Vanilla seeds
Cinnamon
Ground ginger
Ground cumin
Smoked paprika
Chilli powder
1 small dried chilli
Curry powder
Cayenne pepper
Garlic powder

Fresh
Parsley
Rosemary
Coriander
Root ginger

1 stalk lemongrass

Other

16 eggs
1 Nakd bar
Maca powder
Nori strips
Tamari
Vanilla extract
4 cans / cartons (15oz / 400g) chopped tomatoes
8oz / 225g frozen mixed vegetables
Vegetable stock / stock cubes / powder
Himalayan salt
Black pepper

3

Fast Food Week 2

Fresh Veg

3 carrots

4 onions

1 bunch spring onions

2 shallots

4oz / 115g peas (fresh or frozen)

1½lbs / 700g sweetcorn kernels (fresh or frozen)

3¼lbs / 1.5kg parsnips

1 small red beetroot

1 leek

1 head broccoli

2 medium cauliflowers

2lbs / 1kg potatoes

1 sweet potato

4 chestnut mushrooms

6 mushrooms

6 button mushrooms

4 portobello mushrooms

2 courgettes

1 green pepper

1 red pepper

1 yellow pepper

1 tray pre-prepared Mediterranean vegetables

1 bag prepared stir-fry vegetables

1 avocado

6oz / 170g green beans

1 cucumber

1 bunch of kale

1 bag spinach

7oz / 200g bag baby spinach

1 bag of watercress

1 bag baby rocket leaves

1 head of celery

1 punnet cherry tomatoes

1 large tomato

1 tray of salad from supermarket salad bar

2 bulbs of garlic

Fresh Fruit

4 apples

1 banana

1 pound plantains or green bananas

1 punnet strawberries

1 punnet raspberries

1 punnet blackberries

1 lemon

2 limes

1lb / 500g grapes

1 pot prepared chopped fruit

Dried Fruit

Raisins

Apricots

Sultanas

Dates

Figs

Fish & Shellfish

4oz / 115g smoked salmon
6-8 scallops
7oz / 200g cooked and peeled prawns
4 x 6oz / 170g halibut fillets

Nuts & Seeds

Flaxseeds
Chia seeds
Sunflower seeds (7oz / 200g for recipes)
Pumpkin seeds (10½oz / 300g for recipes)
Almonds (9oz / 250g for recipes)
Cashews
Walnuts
Hazelnuts
Brazil nuts

Herbs & Spices

Dried

Marjoram
Oregano
Ground coriander seeds
Basil
Tarragon
Sage
Bouquet garni
Dried mixed herbs
Cinnamon
Ground ginger
Turmeric

Ground cumin
Curry powder
Chilli powder
Chinese 5 spice

Fresh

Coriander
Mint
Basil
Root ginger

Other

1lb / 450g quinoa
9oz / 250g quinoa flakes or brown rice
1 bag (250g) ready cooked brown rice
7oz / 200g wholemeal pasta
3½oz / 100g wholemeal spaghetti
2½oz / 75g porridge oats
8 eggs
1 large (500g) pot natural yogurt
2 small pots natural yogurt
1 Nakd bar
Psyllium husk powder
Nori strips
4 cans / cartons (15oz / 400g) chopped tomatoes
Tomato puree
1 jar capers
1 jar / packet black olives
1 jar / packet sundried tomatoes
Vegetable stock / stock cubes / powder
Himalayan salt
Black pepper
Extra virgin olive oil
Coconut oil

Recipe Index

Smoothies & Juices

Breakfasts

Snacks

Lunch & Supper Dishes

The Body Rescue Detox Recipe Book